MERSEY MINIS

VOLUME THREE

LONGING

edited by

Deborah Mulhearn

Mersey Minis

VOLUME THREE: LONGING

Edited by Deborah Mulhearn
Illustrations by Clare Curtis
Graphic design by Ken Ashcroft
Printed and bound in Italy by Graphicom

ISBN: 978-0-9556547-0-1

First published in August 2007 by Capsica Ltd
83 Ampthill Road, Liverpool L17 9QN, UK

www.merseyminis.com
www.loveliverpoolbooks.com

CONTENTS

Dedicated to the people of Liverpool,
past, present and future

INTRODUCTION

LONGING is the third volume in the Mersey Minis series. The first two Mersey Minis, LANDING and LIVING, are collections of writing about Liverpool through the ages, drawn from historic and contemporary sources, mostly previously published. LONGING, however, contains all new writing specially created in 2007 to celebrate Liverpool's 800th anniversary. It's a one-off, given away free on 28th August 2007, though it appears again within the complete five-volume set.

More than two thirds of the pieces in LONGING result from a competition run by Capsica, the Mersey Minis publisher. The others were commissioned. We asked for a short piece of prose about Liverpool, the Mersey or Merseyside, on the theme of longing. The idea was to mix 'ordinary' voices with established writers and well known names connected with Liverpool and create a sort of photo album full of literary snapshots, all written in 2007, the city's 800th anniversary.

It was a pleasure and a privilege, as Mersey Minis editor, to be part of the panel of judges asked to select the competition entries. But not an easy task, I realised when I started reading. At first they were all clamouring for attention: slices of Liverpool life and longings that I'd either forgotten about or never knew existed. But slowly, distinctive voices started to emerge. Small details of longing stuck with me: wind chimes in a cemetery, a lone dandelion in cracked concrete, the salty lips of a long-ago lover. And then the large sweep of it hit me: for childhood innocence, familiar streetscapes, the love and protection of parents and grandparents.

We all experience longing. It looks forward and back, like our two Pier Head Liver Birds, towards the city and out to sea, or to the future and the past. The two figures on the cover suggest these longings. The sculpture of Eleanor Rigby represents longing for what might have been, and the young girl longs for her life to begin. Perhaps.

The pieces selected weren't necessarily the most polished, but they all have one thing in common besides Liverpool – they come from the heart. It was exciting to receive entries from all over the world, not just from Liverpool. There are obvious longings (Beatles) and obscure longings (bell ringing), but together they create this wonderful Mersey mosaic.

I'd like to thank Arabella and Fiona for giving me the opportunity to be part of LONGING, which has been published without subsidy or sponsorship; the writing competition judges, Jane Davis and Charles Nevin, whose expertise and literary nous kept me from trying to squeeze every entry into the book; and writer Jenny Newman of Liverpool John Moores University who acted as chair. I'd also like to thank illustrator Clare Curtis for her distinctive lino-cuts which beautifully express the bittersweet nature of longing.

Most of all I'd like to thank the writers: the commissioned writers; and those who entered the competition (including those who didn't get through). It takes guts to enter a writing competition, never mind to lay bare your longings, which people have done with precision and passion. These longings have now joined Liverpool's literary current, like raindrops on our broad brown river.

DEBORAH MULHEARN

LONGING

Mike Hyde   *A Liverpolitan*

My father, Thomas Bertram Hyde, lived at 28 St Albans Road, Bootle. His father was manager of the London & Lancashire Insurance Company. When TB left school he had a week in their offices but office life didn't suit him.

So, unusually for his background, he became an apprentice patternmaker with Crichtons. There he made the mistake one day of saying that he had nothing to do and spent the next week in the bowels of a ship hand-drilling a one inch hole through twelve inches of steel.

There may be those who doubt the exactitude of the anecdote but another one was confirmed 30 years later. He was standing in a tram, smoking and carrying me (aged one), an umbrella and a scythe, when it braked to a halt at Commutation Row. He flew the length of the tram, his cigarette dropping into the umbrella. Passers by were greeted by the sight of a man holding a baby and a scythe whilst dancing on a flaming umbrella.

My brother heard Evelyn Waugh relating this spectacle on the wireless 40 years ago. Waugh had witnessed the scene from a passing taxi, no doubt impressed with the singularity of Liverpool life.

I'd love to travel again with my father (without the flames) on the overhead railway and the ferries but being an engineer like him, I have no fanciful idea that this could ever happen.

Jane Bellis   *Lost boys*

Some days you wander the streets by the docks, hoping to find that smile you have lost. Staring at the builders moving cranes over what was once Chavasse Park. The wind carries echoes of dreams your forefathers imagined. Blowing from the clean hills of North Wales, you face the cold weight of expectation it brings.

I see you sometimes by Otterspool in the evenings, on your bike, leaning over the railings with some chips. The river flows on endlessly, miles and miles of dirty Mersey. You smoke your last ciggie and throw the end into the water. Watch as it washes away into the greyness.

Caught between the abyss of childhood and adulthood you haunt the alleys and the paths of Dingle, the woods at St. Michaels and Sefton Park. The school won't touch you now, you turn 16 soon....you are free to enjoy your time. You tuck in behind luxury flats and shiny shopping quarters.

Discontent gnawing away throughout the day, your anger melts into a pool of saliva, gobbed all over the city.

Phil Morris   *Can't get back quick enough*

You've got a heart that sings. You bring a world to my shore. You're a pretty girl with no make up on. You shock me. You scare me. You make me cry. You take the piss. You take risks. You shoot yourself in the foot. You're misunderstood. You've got an inner glow. You've got spirit. You're on everyone's lips. Your reputation precedes you (it keeps the riff-raff out). You're envied and not pitied. You're beauty punctuated with litter and dirt. The sea cleans your breath. You're a mind spoken. You're well cast. You beat your own path. You're a tune we can hum. You're a lyrical passport. You make me proud. You make me sing. You've got time. You've got stories in the lines on your face. You like a drink. You're a lousy cook. You're a conversation on a bus. You stress your 's' and your 't'. You're well dressed in the supermarket. You're a streetwise wily beggar. You're a wise crack followed by a quicker wit. You put yourself down when no one else is allowed. You look after yourself. Your passion spreads like infection. You're born fighting a corner. You're the underdog. You're a nation. You're my bird.

It was only when I left you that I realised who you are.

Mhairi Tynan *Glamorous Granny Sykes*

A great big dining table sometimes, often a small kitchen table, steak and kidney pie. Glamorous Liverpool Granny Sykes in her scarves and good clothes. All the cousins run riot in the garden, thick accents, confusing the ones not from round here I'm not from round here I'm a small visitor. Glamour seems to cling to the very fabric of the house, the smart terrace with its stained glass window on the stairs. I want so much to fit in, to speak like they do, to peer past the adults into the perfumed secrets of Granny's bedroom.

Later, a train journey with my sister, the overwhelming excitement of the docks, Richard and Judy, a man in the dock, telling us it might rain. It always seemed it might, but that would be atmosphere not dreary. An Italian restaurant, where you can sign the tablecloth, far superior to any other, and Granny older yet even more impeccable. Oblivious though, to the cousins downstairs secretly lighting their fags in the loo. At the table (signed only by us) sit the tiny sparkling Aunt, the well-groomed cousin, and us, still in awe of this Mersey sheen.

Phone calls in between irregular trips to the fog, the pointing to the Cavern – Dad went there as a lad (I am still incredibly proud of this link to credibility, beyond all reason) – the modern cathedral which Granny doesn't like, and wonderful, impractical, expensive dresses bought lovingly for my tiny daughter. Granny Sykes sweeps through the streets, carrying me in her wake, and all around I swivel to see laughter, people, those voices. It's nothing I can grab hold of but I want to take it home, let it fill my life.

Even the nursing home can't dull the excitement of our trips to Liverpool. The house is gone, but now there is a pub where the tiny Aunt makes a funny, caustic landlady, and I am still the tall, gawky one. I want to wear heels and jeans, sequins, leopard print, all of this, not fade away chatting to Uncle Chris, kind and quiet.

Much later, a coffin, carried towards the end. The pub is sold, the aunt abroad and I long once more for a friendly sitting room, a cup of tea and an entry ticket to the inner life I glimpsed.

Helen Glasspoole   *Home*

Thrust into the turbulence of warring Liverlines and Merseybuses I travel Smithdown Road.

Past cathedrals, I walk down the hill where university mingles with other life – less transient life; real life? I near Lime Street Station – my connection to familiar places. I enter the chaos of markets and shopping centres and the docks

with shops not meant for student grants. Tinny music on a ferry across the Mersey. Beatles songs playing at the Cavern. Late night talks.

I tune my ear to hear the voice of my new home. A stranger in the city that is home – wanting to be a part of it, to own it, to feel included.

Frank Cottrell-Boyce   *Permanent sandstone sunrise*

There can't be many things more fun than making a film in your home town. The glamour of film is a key that opens mysterious, forbidden doorways. On the pretext of recce-ing locations, I've visited the control room at Lime Street Station, stood on top of the Liver Building and walked along the pedestrian service tunnel that runs beneath the Queensway Mersey tunnel. During filming I've been party to sticking a statue of Lenin in front of the Cunard building and filling the square with snow; and to turning a derelict plot in the Dingle into a flourishing vegetable garden. But the most fun in filming your home town comes in editing, when a series of cuts can make a character, if you want, turn left at the end of Church Street and wind up in Formby Woods, or stroll out of Lime Street Station, onto a beach. You can cut up and collage your city to your heart's content. And erase. The fun I've had wiping out hideous precincts and flyovers, reconnecting the waterfront to the city centre, removing the philistine shopping developments from Chavasse Park and replacing them with a fitting memorial to Liverpool's bravest son. Of course an unerase facility would be nice too – I'd love to put back the original castle on Castle Street, the ancient abbey, the two massive granite pillars that once rose out of the sea, marking the entrance to the river channel. But what I really yearn for is a menu that would allow me to bring to view some of the big, dreamy projects that never made it to the skyline. There's an imaginary Liverpool somewhere where Alsop's *Cloud* building wraps the reflections of the other Graces round itself beside the river; where the Anglican Cathedral has three towers instead of one, and a glass bridge rainbowing over the sorrowful vale of its cemetery to Gambier Terrace; and where the vertiginous hubris of Lutyen's original plans for the Catholic Cathedral – a building so huge you could see it miles out to sea – soars over everything like an eternal stone sunrise. That's the Liverpool I yearn for, a Liverpool where every fabulous, thwarted hope is finally realised for everyone to see.

Angela Barlow   *Edible architecture*

I've always had a strange obsession with the White Star Line offices in James Street. Yet again this candy striped master-

piece, with its hooped turrets of copper and cream, stirred me from my rush hour-induced slumber as I crept along the dock road this morning. Ever since I visited Liverpool as a wide-eyed seven year old Boltonian, I've had a sneaky feeling the White Star building actually has an edible façade. I remember looking longingly and almost salivating at the prospect of a huge building encased in chocolate and icing. So far I have resisted giving its auburn bricks a cheeky lick, so I'd like to think there's still a small chance it could be Liverpool's equivalent of the Hansel and Gretel gingerbread house.

Wandering around the city, I wondered if there were any more buildings in Liverpool with culinary characteristics and discovered that the Radio City tower is a marshmallow ripe for melting, and the columns of the Walker art gallery bear more than a slight resemblance to sticks of coltsfoot rock. Ah, if only Sir Edwin Lutyens' Catholic cathedral had made it past the planning stage, Liverpool would have been home to an ice cream sundae of mammoth proportions.

William Backshall   *The Scaldy*

I learned to swim in the Cut. On summer days, we lads would scale the canal wall adjacent to our terrace house, undress on the towpath, and with those of us able to boast a swimming costume hurriedly changing, the rest would jump or dive into the dark canal waters with whoops of delight. The centre of attraction was a huge submerged pipe on the far bank constantly discharging pleasantly hot water from the grimy rubber-works boiler room. This was known far and wide as the Scaldy, which, over many years attracted boys with its free entertainment. In addition to swimming, youths would bring along bars of soap, and enjoy an al fresco bath, though whether they emerged cleaner was doubtful.

Others would daub their bodies in bizarre patterns with the clay that surrounded the area, and after cavorting around in imitation war dances of Redskin Indians seen at the local movie matinee, they would then jump into the waters and emerge again as palefaces.

Older lads engaged recognised swimming styles, whilst we kids adopted what was known as 'doggy'. I eventually learnt to dive, progressing from belly flops that left my stomach red and smarting, to an improved crab-like entry. At the bottom of the dive the water was inky black, and surfacing, it would change to a dark brown, then lighter brown, becoming clear only inches from the top. What a brew! Why we never came down with dreadful diseases, I'll never understand. Another hazard was the neighbourhood rubbish that lay jettisoned on the bottom, old beds and bike wheels, ensuring great care had to be taken not to become entangled.

A longed-for attraction would be the sighting of a laden barge towed by a magnificent, unattended shire horse. Other activities ceased as we ran to welcome this greater source of delight. The barge was soon boarded by lads who then ran along the side decks before diving in, repeating the exercise many times. An added thrill was dodging the  small pieces of coal thrown by the bargee from his bunker, whilst he was stationed at the tiller.

The fun would pall as the barge progressed beyond our home waters, then the bargee would be left in peace as we returned to our beloved Scaldy. I recall those barge men as being dour, speaking what seemed to be a foreign language, and curiously, wearing wooden boots that made a loud knocking noise as they chased us off their craft.

One friendly bargee, finally abandoned by the boarding

natives, tucked the tiller under his arm, re-lit his pipe, smiled, and gave us a slow wave of goodbye. 'Ta ra, Mister,' we chorused and waved back, and I wonder even now, whether he was remembering, as I do, happy carefree boyhood days.

David Bateman   *Starting up*

Jamaica Street. Past garages and warehouses in the hissing rain, I trudge away from Training For Work at Queen's Dock, on my way to visit the dole for the last time. The sky's so dark, you wouldn't believe it's only just the end of August. But I'm on a mission.

Since I was sixteen, I was always going to be a writer. I still remember that sunny June weekend, buying a book of poetry on my way home from my Saturday job. I recognized the poets' names from an LP I'd heard: Henri, McGough and Patten. They were funny and serious at the same time, and, reading the book that evening, I suddenly remembered a dream I'd had, and thought maybe I could make a poem out of that. Next day, at risk of being thought airy-fairy, I showed the poem to a couple of friends; and I was always going to be a writer from then on. Admittedly I stuttered so badly I didn't know if I'd ever be able to talk properly; but at least I could write.

On Jamaica Street, the passing cars are spreading great whooshes of spray behind them, and I'm keeping as far from the kerb as I can.

Since 1980, it's been unemployment punctuated by part-time jobs, temporary jobs, training schemes. But this scheme I've just finished was about self-employment. And this time I've got a start-up grant.

15

My jacket is already soaked through. If I blow at the tip of my nose I can send a fine line of spray ahead of me.

It probably looks like I'm just walking along Jamaica Street in the rain. But really I'm on a mission. I am on the road to success.

*****

The magic moment: it's time to sign off. In the office off Tithebarn Street, Gerald indicates the section in my signing-on book I need to fill in.

I hesitate over employer's name and address, then carefully write SELF-EMPLOYED, and my own address.

The next section is easier. It asks me my position.

In neat capitals I write: POET.

*****

And this is it: the first morning... David Bateman is now a self-employed poet, trading under his own name from today, 1st September 1998. In the poet's lofty eyrie in Gambier Terrace, business is very quiet for the first hour, but at 10.10 a.m. the phone rings. Now read on.

'Hello, is Mr Mercer there?' a man's voice asks.

'No, there's no Mr Mercer here,' I say, and tell him my number. Notice how fluently I did that, without a single stutter. I can do that these days, mostly. I even teach Creative Writing classes; and I can perform my poetry without stuttering at all.

'Oh, I've got the wrong number,' says the man. 'Sorry.'

'That's okay,' I tell him. 'Goodbye.'

'Goodbye.'

I put the phone down, and return to a piece I'm writing about walking along Jamaica Street in the rain. In the distance, standing in a sunny place beneath a gap in the clouds, fame and fortune are waving, beckoning.

Leto Martinou Kyritsi   *The poet's house*

On Huskisson Street stands unassuming the two-hundred year old house of the Hellene poet, Constantine Cavafy; the one who came to be known as the Alexandrian. He shared his early life between Egypt, London and Liverpool, where he spent five years, before retiring to Lepsius Street in Alexandria, to live austerely – and write *Ithaca, Awaiting the Barbarians* and *God Forsakes Anthony*; to live with fervour – and write dimly lit, erotic elegies about anonymous boys with eyes like black holes. Many afternoons I would leave M at home to wrestle with the demons and wizards of the World of Warcraft, and go for solitary long walks that would often lead me to Cavafy's old neighbourhood. I used to stand for a few moments outside the house as if to pay my respects; then I would slowly walk up and down the street, observing every corner, daydreaming of the day when I would be able to make the house of the poet mine. In the afternoon, I would leave the windows half-open. Would the air still be heavy with musky aromas? Or thick with smoke from expensive tobacco? Would the smoke lift to reveal more spectres of dark-eyed boys, wanting me to let the poet know of their devotion? The poet would then do his duty and elevate the beautiful spectres into triumphant immortality, never communicating to them the futility of 'nights of sensual delight, or its bright mornings'. Himself he would choose to exit in silence. My typewriter – in my mind, always a typewriter – would echo stolen inspiration and yet be generously goaded on by it. To strike a pose, I wouldn't have to smoke a pipe like he did; I'd just let my hair loose. In that house, emotion would be channelled into disciplined streams of ink that would etch eternity onto paper as eager as skin. Daydreaming happened on many occasions; each time, one step closer to making the Ouija board of inspiration speak up. And then, suddenly, the invisible troupe of reality appeared, with its music and shouts, and Liverpool was snatched from my sights.

Gill Norton   *Liverpool Bay*

In the late summer when the weather is fine and the tide is as far out as it will go, I walk out across the long stretch of shore to the edge of the sea and look out across Liverpool Bay and the coastline to Formby Point. The wind turbines turn lazily, gleaming white in the sun and the returning Irish Ferry is just visible on the skyline.

Through muddy inshore patches and encroaching sea grasses, past the skeleton ribs of the old wooden boat, I walk onto the great spaces of clean washed sand, part soft, part ridged and firm, until I reach the water's edge. The houses behind me are no longer visible and the black, square still-remaining sections of the long-ago wrecked coaster emerge from the sea ahead.

A lone seal raises his doggy head and watches as the terns dive bomb fish. He sees me. I wade slowly into the sun-warmed sea and float, relaxed and peaceful, looking up at the wide expanse of blue sky, alone – this is my paradise, the place where I always long to be.

David Morrissey   *Kenny*

I lived the first eight years of my life at 45 Seldon Street in Kensington, or 'Kenny' as we called it. They were back to back houses linked by endless cobbled streets that seemed to go on forever. A huge brick maze that I alone had the map for and knew like the back of my hand.

The house itself had three rooms downstairs. The front room that faced out onto the street was considered my mum and dads' room and had their TV in it. Then there was the back room which was very much my Nan's room and that led onto a kitchen. Then out into a small back yard with a coal hole and an outside loo. Upstairs there were three bedrooms. My two brothers had one room, my sister shared a room with my Nan, and then there was my mum and dads' room which I also slept in. It seems inconceivable to me now that we all lived in that space. I can't imagine how the adults had a bath for example. Us kids had a tin bath in the kitchen, but how did they manage?

It wasn't always harmonious, far from it at times, but it seemed to work, and at least everyone else in the street was living in the same way. We had some good friends there, and I was in and out of our neighbours' houses as much as my own.

Then in the early 70s the bulldozers came and took away the surrounding streets. It opened up a giant playground for us. We'd build dens out of the debris, battlefields and castles, a treasure trove of discarded furniture and faded photos, until, one by one, my gang disappeared. Every week another member had to pack up and go. All of us flung across the North West like refugees, starting new lives in strange-sounding places like Skelmersdale, Runcorn and Kirkby. And for us, Knotty Ash.

A brand new estate. Four bedrooms and a bathroom! Even a downstairs loo. And a garden, which was full of builders clay when we moved in. But with lots of digging from my dad and tender loving care from my mum it became quite a reasonable football pitch, come cricket field, come tennis court.

The move was welcomed by all of us. We needed to move and besides we didn't have a choice. But my mum must have had mixed emotions about it. Great to have some space and a bathroom. But she'd been born in Kenny, gone to school there, survived the war there, courted, married, had four kids and lost her father there. But I guess the promise of inside plumbing and mowing your own lawn were enough for her to march into the future without too much of a backward glance.

Shirley Buckley   *The long and winding road*

Liverpool is a city of saints, its churches, schools, social clubs and markets. It's where you can eat bacon ribs and Scouse with red pickled cabbage and drink in Irish pubs and argue about football until you're red or blue in the face. Liverpool is a city on the water, on the edge, on the up and sometimes on its arse. Liverpool is a place where you'll be fed and given a bed for the night after a Grand National fiasco. Liverpool is a place of dark shadows and dodgy deals and bright, wild nightclub lights and lively birds of many virtues and some vices in every bar. Liverpool was a place where lovers dreamed dreams by the old canal and kissed their girls by the factory wall; of vibrant docks and Tate and Lyle and a money-hungry slave trader who gave his name to Penny Lane when a penny was obviously worth more than it is today. Liverpool is a city built on religious rivalry where your father might have been orange and your mother green yet their places of worship were joined at the hip by a street named Hope. Liverpool is the place where a young man grieved when he thought about his darling on leaving Prince's

Landing Stage for California and where a statue of a man stands stark naked, testicles on display to every passing shopper and where Bridget McCann dreamt of having fifty kids and a house in Speke. Liverpool was on Hitler's hit list. He forced my Grandma to shelter under a bridge by the docks with what remained of her brood, the others having been farmed out to Shropshire. And they all thanked God afterwards that the Pier Head was still there. Liverpool is a city on the water; a place that has nearly drowned many a time through lack of interest or political mayhem or gizza-job indifferences but like the phoenix has risen from the ashes only her bird is a liver bird, alive-alive-oh. Liverpool is a city where the beat goes on and where you'll still find a yellow submarine although this one has mutated into a bus that looks like a duck. Liverpool knows how to reinvent itself. It is a city of longing: longing for the past, the present and the future. Despite the hard knocks, the spirit is always willing though the flesh is sometimes weak.

Sue Haasler   *Red in the head*

Pool of red, sea of green, *Li-verpool! Li-verpool!* all around me. But I'm 160 miles north-east of Anfield, at Roker Park, Sunderland. It's a Saturday afternoon in November 1976, and I've pestered my mum to bring me to my first ever football match. I'm desperate to see Liverpool and I insist on standing with the away supporters, because I'm already Liverpudlian in my heart. For the first time in my sixteen year old Geordie life I'm surrounded by Scousers, and I love it. It's like being in an episode of *The Liver Birds* with added swearing, though the lad behind us with the long ginger hair apologises charmingly to my mum for his language. She's not listening anyway – she's watching the effect of drizzle on Ray Kennedy's shorts. And when super-sub David Fairclough comes on and scores the winning goal, and everyone around me goes barmy, I'm mentally going west myself.

Dea Parkin   *City lover*

Liverpool. Like a lover, like an undependable, kiss-and-flee, love-you-leave-you-love-you charmer. Not so much a ne'er do well, more a don't-stay-long-enough-to-tell. Defying commitment to category. Always flirting with tomorrow, dancing on the grave of your past. When will I ever know you? Sparkling in the light, moody in the shadow. Exciting. Stimulating. Passionate. I like that in a city.

David Swift   *A justified boast*

As an absent Liverpudlian do I pine? No. Am I proud? Oh yes yes yes. And exuberant, oh yes. Because of where we are going. Defeatism has gone for good. We now have the conscience to face our part-shameful distant history. As we had the forthrightness much more recently to condemn recent scavengers who sought municipal self-importance from our civic impoverishment. Exploitation and contraction are discarded experiences.

It once took effort for a self-willed absentee native to return, other than to Anfield, Goodison Park, the Walker and the Tate. No more. Our past today is prime talk. We long for the greatness of the past but without its grievous scars. We want a new foundation. A new beginning. We're aspirational. But it's a justified boast. It's talk of the future: of the near future and the future future; of 2008 and well beyond. And yes our Great Past is scarred with some terrible warts. Warts that can never be forgotten. But by their recognition and eradication we can now move forward with a new energy that will embolden our revival and enliven our future.

Clare Bunting   *Bold Street*

I caught my first glimpse of Liverpool when I was just eighteen and a student at John Moores. '*Big Issue, Big Issue*. Anyone for a *Big Issue*?' a man chanted as I made my way to HSBC. This scruffy-looking man dressed in army jacket and black jeans walked towards me. I couldn't think of how to get away, so I put my hand in my pocket and gave him a pound, not knowing if that was enough. He smiled as he snatched it away. 'It's my last one, love. Do you mind if I keep it?' he said clutching on to the magazine. His comment took me by surprise. I smiled back and walked on.

I could hear jazz coming from a side street. I made my way for it, stopping to glance at the Caribbean coloured cocktail dresses in the window of Karen Millen. The soft tones of rhythm and blues led me up Bold Street. I don't remember seeing the saxophonist's face but I can't forget the flutter I felt inside as he played. I wanted to leap up and down and

wave my hands about, shouting 'This is my new home. I've arrived.'

I spied a funky furniture shop, a red velvet chaise longue moulded into the shape of a pair of lips adorning the front window. This was followed by an art shop, a retro clothes boutique

where the most popular students shopped, a gift shop flaunting the latest essentials for the home: mosaic photo room dividers, opaque glass espresso cups and saucers and a range of arty cards made with fabric and gold sequins. At the very top of the street stood Café Tabac, a little piece of foreignness where groups of cool art students liked to hang out and talk about their complicated lives. As I stood on the corner looking out towards the burnt-out church overgrown with trees, I was almost blown away by a bitter wind. I never did get used to that Mersey breeze. As the wind changed, I saw my new life wrapped up in this tiny little cobbled street and I couldn't wait to be a part of it.

Dave Ward   *Hale shore and lighthouse*

One lone lighthouse stands at the river's edge, where low cliffs of crumbling earth slither down to the muddy sand below. This is where the vast emptiness of the sky meets the Mersey where it slides in a wide swooping curve towards the city which lurks out of sight round the corner, before drifting slowly on to the sea.

This is where song-larks rise into the towering air above the slope of the fields, where wild rabbits scurry from hidden burrows, where reed warblers sway on the stems of tall grass.

This is where the giant gangling frame of the Childe of Hale may have come, may never have come at all, to peer out at those hills which are jewelled now with the windows of the chemical works which sit like palaces of glittering silence across the dull water on the opposite side.

This is where the grey geese gather, swooping and squawking, their tail feathers rattling a metallic warning as they crash land on the meadow flats to peck and to harry, then raise their long necks, ignoring the clumsy roar of planes taking off, to peer at the world which is *their* world: this solitude where one lone heron patrols the wind-swept shore.

Karen Lamb   *Internet dating*

Big Dipper girl *weary of the Roller Coaster and ready for the Big One.*
Lecturer of Luv *dizzy from dissertations and ready to graduate beyond comprehension.*

On seeing smiles we double clicked and e-mailed thereafter. On reading lines of invisible ticking boxes we suspected a sweet explosion afoot and progressed to the phone. On hearing laughter we knew we had to step out of the cables and pixels onto the platform. And so it began with a Saver Open-of-hopefully-no Return.

We met at Lime Street Station, hand smiles and nervous shakes, and then made haste to Turner at the Tate. We tittle-tattled to impress with impressionism and modernism. We eyed each other through undulating Henry Moore curves when all we really wanted was to impress our curves into each other and undulate. Waltzing in the Walker we delved into Doves and Dreams of the Glasgow Four. Gingerly treading, cat-like in Macintosh. Flippancy and flirting flourished around forms in Formby. And at Speke we glimmered the unspoken, touching my breast as he lifted me into the Ha-ha.

Later, hoping in Hope Street I turned corners into Bold. We fumbled fingers at Fact, took a fast car to his, and gave our all in Allerton.

Jan Minting   *A different view*

November. We pick our way through the stones, unsuitable heels poking stiletto holes into the ground. A biting wind cuts through the rows of strangers, strangers lying toe to toe, declaring their lives for all to see. 'What do you think love?' The cheery voice is real, holds a genuine empathy. 'If you choose that one he'll look towards Runcorn and Widnes, but this one means he'll face towards Liverpool. Take your time, there's no rush.'

Knowsley Cemetery, Dad's final resting place. Next Wednesday, we'll bring him here and leave him forever. I'm scared he won't be happy and I'm scared he'll be cold and I need to tell him I'll bring flowers and cards and candles and... I can't.

Mum points to the ground. 'This one,' she says. We all nod in agreement whether we agree or not, but I know we do.

Now I stand and look at the view. The sun is shining and the visiting flowers nod their heads to the tinkle of wind chimes on the breeze. I don't feel a biting wind. The strangers are my friends, I know all their names and their silence beckons the future, not the past.

Almost three years. I turn, slowly, 360 degrees. The horizon hasn't changed, I just noticed it. The houses on Lickers Lane, the golf club on the hill, the M62; distant traffic, droning bees.

Me and Dad now face the same direction. I look towards the city, the city full of our lives, loves and memories.

I rest my hand on the headstone, like putting my arm around his shoulder. It's been a long journey and I wish I could tell him, but I think he already knows.

'Dad,' I whisper, 'We're home.'

Margaret Murphy   *The kindness of strangers*

They say you should never go back, but in a sense I'd never left. Shipped from Runcorn by coach to our Liverpool grammar school for eighteen months, me and my sisters became educational commuters.

I had to go back. But it wasn't a hankering for place, for friends – the touchstones of streets and neighbours and shops that I knew – but a slow realisation that I didn't belong where I'd been put.

My interview was one of the last. I can't remember how I travelled – bus? – train? There was no help from my parents: 'You want it so much, you can sort yourself out.'

The clock tower of the university's Victoria Building was my landmark, my landfall. The mist that had kept its distance all day, crept slowly in from the Mersey. By steady accretion, it inched up the buildings and sank into basement laboratories, obscuring signs, homogenising the ugly clutter of Victorian redbrick and nineteen-sixties concrete. Fog. It gathered, cold and clammy, dense as poured milk. Blinding, threatening.

I was lost, and late. My heart pounding, I tried another way. Came up against another blind alley. Turned again, retraced my steps, found again the black railings that edged the cytology department. Opposite, beyond the gated archway, invisible in the murk, the muted swish of traffic; on the river, a foghorn mourned.

I stared at the useless map, then plunged once more into the fog.

'Are you lost, love?' A porter, comforting in his blue uniform.

Distraught, I was able only to nod miserably.

He showed me to the door.

I left half an hour later with a firm offer. The fog hadn't lifted – there was no symbolic mark of nature's assent. But the lamps in the jostle of quads and alleys were now lit, each beatified by a circle of scattered light. I couldn't see the path, but I could feel it, step by tentative step. And I knew I could always ask someone the way.

Stephen McKay   *Hiraeth*

Despite being a Yorkshireman born and bred I have to admit my love for a piece of old Lancashire. After living in Liverpool for nearly twenty years, looking across the Mersey, I am now working at the other end of the M62, on the east coast looking out over the Humber.

I am experiencing, for the first time in my life, what the Welsh call 'hiraeth'. It doesn't have a direct translation – it means 'longing' but it's the sort of longing to be home that is so strong it makes you ill and stops you sleeping.

The emigrant Scouser singing a few lines of *Ferry Cross the Mersey* will shed the same tear as the Welsh exile singing *The Old Land of My Fathers*.

When I come home now, my heart leaps at the sight of the Liver Birds on their Pier Head perch. They have the same patina that gives each nook and cranny of Liverpool its unique character. Liverpool is cosmopolitan; as a port city it has always welcomed visitors and those of us who stay are proud to be called Scousers, even if only by those unfortunates who don't love the city as we do. Adopted Scousers extol the virtues of their new home with a missionary zeal.

The traditional pubs of Liverpool are the bastions of a culture that constantly changes but like the famous Liverpool dish, scouse is delicious no matter what goes into it. I'm never more happy than when I'm snug in the snug of a Liverpool pub talking to native born Scousers like my friends Yusuf, Bernie and Ronnie Soo.

Here in Hull it is too quiet; I miss the black cabs running like molasses down Lime Street, the fat lasses rolling in the gutters of Mathew Street at closing time, the smell of Chinese restaurants mixing with the evocative odour of chip-shop curry and kebabs on Renshaw Street. I miss the cacophony of music blasting out from the shady doorways of Wood Street but most of all I miss the Scousers – those loud, no nonsense, wonderful Scousers.

Outside my Humberside apartment, where no one stirs, is a finger-post, part of the Cross-Pennine Trail, pointing west. On it is the single word, a word of hope, an inspirational word, the word 'Liverpool'.

The fabled river has been close to me, a companion through my life, always there, constant as the call of a seagull and the timeless tides that flow each and every day.

As a child I would sit having my tea in a now demolished tenement block, while my boyhood eyes would watch the Liverpool ships and sailors sail down the river to far-off

adventures in mysterious lands across the oceans. Destinations such as Africa, India, the Americas, Arabia. How I longed to swap places with a Liverpool sailor on such a journey. And sometimes I would lie awake listening to the mournful sigh of a fog-horn in the lonely hours of the night.

Yes, the fabled river is in my blood. One grandfather worked building those ships in Cammell Laird, while the other was a docker. My dad was a ship's painter, and he would take me down to the dry dock to see the big ships newly painted. I often dreamt that one day I would be the captain on such a ship and it would be me sailing to the other side of the world.

We would stop at a docker's canteen for tea and toast on a winter's morning. I'd sit there listening to the men making their bets for the day or talking about the ship they were working on. I would drink my mug of tea while steam ran down cracked windows. There was such a sense of belonging, of friendship, of comradeship even thought I was only a young lad still trying to feel my way in the world. That was a time when real jobs were done on the docks before they became apartments and retail outlets. Do we still hear the ghosts of those dockers whispering on the cold Mersey wind?

Jennifer Moore *You say goodbye and I say hello*

Every teenager yearns for escape, craving new horizons. At fifteen I flew all the way to America, only to find Liverpool waiting there for me. At the Hard Rock Cafe, Orlando, I bought the book, got the t-shirt and came away with a John Lennon recording and a tiny packet of dust for good measure. Not just any dust, you understand. Cavern Club dust.

Jeff Young *Ghosts*

He was an old man when he went blind so my grandad had already memorised the city. He could tell you which back yards had dairy cows in and where to place an illegal bet. He looked like a proper old man – boots, navvy suit and flat cap – and there was an indentation the size of an old penny on the side of his skull where,

folklore had it, he had had radium implants to correct his failing vision. He lived in a house where the cellar was rumoured to contain the rising waters of a secret tributary of the Mersey, and he once told me the Aurora

Borealis was visible from the rooftops of every house in Grey Rock Street if the moon was behind a cloud. Such is the mythology.

The city was being demolished and my grandfather couldn't see it disappearing. Every day he would walk the same route, along the same pavements, down the same back entries, to the same corner shop, past the same sweet factory. In the city centre, other old men watched the old market coming down and the new concrete precinct coming up. The men were sad; they didn't like what they were seeing – but at least they could see it. My grandfather could only feel the demolition, the percussion of collapsing buildings reverberating through his bones.

This was not nostalgia – this was empathy. My grandfather *was* the city and as the city was reduced so was he. The city's soul was being removed and my grandfather's soul crumbled accordingly, like the brick and sandstone all around him.

Today you can sit in a Liverpool pub beneath photographs of men long gone. I have looked for years for a photograph of my grandfather on these walls. He was a carter and there are many pictures of men in flat caps, standing proudly by their horses, delivering sacks of hops to the brewery. This is my longing. I once saw his ghost on Lodge Lane outside Maguires Livery Stable but it was a too fleeting vision and he was gone before I could reach out to hold him.

These men are the true guardians of our city. Their dignity and bearing lends them an air of watchfulness. The sense of helplessness I often experience when I walk through our city makes me feel close to what those men must have felt when they said their quiet goodbyes to their homes, pubs and market lanes.

My grandfather had a map inside his heart of the city he had lived in all his life. He couldn't see the bulldozers, couldn't see the houses falling. He would walk along the desolate wasteland streets, his inner compass guiding him past the ghosts of dead architecture, through the city of his memory and imagination.

And in his last sightless days he was still walking through the city he had lived in for more than 80 years... even though it was no longer there.

Jane Bradley   *The end of the world*

I was born in Liverpool in 1984, in a hospital that has long since burned down. The year that George Orwell predicted the end of the world, and instead there was just the aftermath of the Toxteth riots, and me.

My mother was still a student then. She went into labour seven weeks early; bent double in her lecture at the Polytechnic, a mess of water at her feet. She was meant to give birth to me on Boxing Day. I should've been a Christmas baby. Instead I arrived shrunken and blue on Hallowe'en, and was kept in an incubator for weeks. Apparently there were several times when I nearly died. Years later, in a run-down pub on Wavertree High Street when I was seventeen, my Dad would slur to me with his whiskey-breath that I was the most precious of all his children. It had been the most difficult keeping me alive.

When I was a toddler we lived in a house on Percy Street, one of those huge Victorian ones with the steep moss-slimed steps going up to the doors. Years later, after Mum and Dad had married and then divorced, they would read in the tabloids that old, old artwork by Lennon and McCartney had been found in a disused attic on our street. They checked around, and of course it was in the house we had had. All that time, and we never knew about the fortune above us, thickly coated with cobwebs and dust. We could have been millionaires, Mum told me. Too late for that kind of talk now.

After the Percy Street flat we shared a squat with eight other students in a house near Sefton Park. I remember the huge wrought-iron gates and the paint flaking off to show the rust underneath. Glass houses full of tropical plants, the air hot and humid, and Mum stealing sips from Dad's can of cider as I pulled with chubby hands at the plastic buckles fastening me into my pram.

Other times we'd go to the crumbly red cathedral; a strange bohemian parody of a normal Sunday family picnic. Mum and Dad would share a cheap bottle of wine in the overgrown gardens while I picked flowers for the most neglected and forgotten-looking graves. Always sympathetic towards the underdog, even then. And sometimes from inside if we got the timing right there'd be organ music, weddings or funerals or Sunday services. The sound of bells and choirs, but distorted as it came through the lurid stained glass, as if it were coming from underwater, or far away, or ghosts.

Roger McGough   *Something for the weekend*

When I saw the sign outside a barber's shop on Renshaw Street which said,

'Free beer with every haircut. Saturday afternoons' I should have gone in.

'A light trim please, and half of bitter.

Yes, just a little more off the sides, and two bottles of Guinness.

You can leave the back as it is, and twelve cans of Special Brew.

No, nothing for the weekend thank you.

Oh, alright then, I'll take a barrel of Theakston's Old Peculiar.

Cheers. See you next week.'

David Dowling   *From Brooklyn to Bootle*

Sailing past the Statue of Liberty in the soft July rain was something that will live with me forever. I am one of the crew on board the *Liverpool 08* yacht taking part in the Round the World Yacht race.

As we sailed past this famous landmark, I was struck with how much the Hudson River reminded me of the Mersey and of how much I had fallen in love with the city that never sleeps. I remember John Lennon saying something about the Big Apple being a bigger Liverpool, and I have to say you were spot on again John. The only problem, I'm sure we both found, was trying to find a decent chippy here.

The chippy on a Friday tea time, going to watch the blues and a few bevvies in town – sometimes this was all I could think of as I clipped my harness from my life belt onto a solid part of the boat. Battling the cruel elements and the unforgiving Atlantic Ocean, desperate for some more kip and to be a bit warmer, I often joked that I thought I'd won a cruise and that I should be excused from actually trying to win the race itself by working. But we were now heading homeward with only 3,500 miles to go before we sailed across the Mersey to be greeted by thousands which would include my partner Liz, my family and my friends. I felt a love and longing for not just these people in my life but for the city of Liverpool itself.

I had waited a very long time to actually take my place on board the *Liverpool 08* clipper, and all this time I longed to

 be part of it, almost every waking minute was filled with how I was going to sail the ocean, and yes it's true that my mind was on other things but Liverpool, but that July morning leaving Battery Park harbour, I felt a profound and deep desire for one thing only – to get back home.

Walter Menzies   *Shot dead*

Head resting on the cold white tiles above the urinal as he pissed. Fag smouldering. Eyes shut. Tear rolling down his pale cheek. Strangely quiet through in the bar, for a Tuesday night after work. Talking. Murmuring. No laughing and shouting. Violently crumpled Walker's crisp packets expanding in slow-motion from big green glass ashtrays.

Droplets of bitter cruising down the pint glasses. Soaked up by the Higsons beer mats featuring cartoon Liverpool characters: Pierre Head, Anne Field. Pall of blue ciggy smoke softening the shiny mahogany bar, the copper table tops, the nicotine ceiling.

The Grapes in Mathew Street. Not just another quick pint on the way home on a winter Tuesday. Not just another Tuesday. Tuesday December 9th 1980. The day John Lennon died. They day John Lennon was shot dead in New York. The Grapes, only a few yards from where it began, the Cavern. Where it began, the long and winding road to fame, celebrity, death – gunned down in the street by a maniac.

People coming in for a drink. Or something. To be with other people. To be in a crowd. To be in Mathew Street. Some of them weeping. Shock, sadness, loss.

Street door bursts noisily open. Heads turn. It's the woman who sells the Echo, a bundle of papers under her arm. 'Echo! Echo! Echo!' Front page banner headline screams 'JOHN LENNON SHOT DEAD CRAZED GUNMAN CHARGED'.

'Hey doll' shouts a drinker 'gimme allofthem...be worth a lot one day.' Muted snorts of laughter. Heads shaking in disbelief. This is Liverpool. Imagine.

Betty Norton   *What culture, what capital?*

I didn't see Yoko Ono's photographs except on TV. Was that culture? Was it a joke, or a con trick? Next year Liverpool will be the Capital of Culture. What culture is it that they mean? Not the culture of the musicians who took classes at Newsham Park school: that is closed; not the culture of the street entertainers, the pub comedians; I hope it isn't the trendy culture that dips a curtsy to a false Celtic image; surely Liverpool is more intelligent than that? Surely it must be the culture of all the people, including ethnic English, who lived there and contributed; and the sea and ship building and sailors must come into it too; not just the horrors of the slave trade, but the fight to end it; culture is the business of how people live where they are and what they make of their community, whoever they are. Culture is more than a clever trendy play or photos that break the rules to no purpose. Liverpool culture is people like me who were born of it and look back; Liverpool culture is the people who live there now and all the varied lives they lead.

Culture cannot be imposed from outside, nor claimed by the fashion of the moment; it needs to be known and felt by the people who live it. I can only hope for the best.

Gladys Mary Coles   *Liverpool hiraeth*

As a child I was regularly separated from my city, taken across the border to my other childhood world – North Wales. Always there was a keen tug at the centre of my being, a physical sensation which I couldn't express in words. Now I know it was a feeling of displacement. Much as I loved the mountains, the greenery and tumbling waterfalls of my other place, I always experienced sharp longing for Liverpool. Returning to the warm, sooty sandstone of my grandparents' big house was like being embraced by a loving friend. I was soon at one again with the gritty texture of the streets, the familiar shops (especially T J Hughes), Newsham

Park, the tattiness, the rich, individual characters and the voices of home.

Later, another separation came, exiling me to live and study in London. I knew then I was experiencing the hiraeth for Liverpool, to use the Welsh word meaning intense longing for home.

On one occasion, in Oxford Street Marks & Spencer, I heard unmistakably the accents of Liverpool (and there are various kinds of Liverpool accent as Willy Russell shows in *Shirley Valentine*). Loud and clear the voices of these Liverpool Shirleys on a shopping spree rose from the cardigan racks. I followed the women around the store like a sniffer dog pursuing a scent. Just to hear the sounds of home. I tracked after them to Euston Station and almost boarded the 6.20 to Lime Street. I stood at the barrier and imagined myself on that train, coming through the cuttings as it pulled into Lime Street Station, the lovely yellow-stone canyons with the old street-names still pinned to them, and here and there a green plant clinging to the rockface. I saw myself emerging from the front entrance of the station and crossing Lime Street to the plateau of St George's Hall. Here I would greet the four lions I've loved since childhood, when my Uncle Andy used to take me to the Remembrance Sunday ceremony on the plateau. These are friendly lions with faces like those of the huge tabby cats my grandmother kept – like but unlike the aloof lions of Trafalgar Square.

Even today, I say hello to my Liverpool lions on arriving home.

Deborah Singmaster   *Driving seat*

When I last went to Liverpool and stayed, as usual, with my friend Beth (I've changed her name in case she reads this and feels embarrassed), I learned something unexpected about her.

We had planned to spend a morning doing touristy things like walking from St George's Hall down to Pier Head, past the Cavern and the Town Hall – still all new to me. Beth lives out near Sefton Park and we waited by the bus stop with a few other people for a bus to take us into the city centre. It was a sunny, windy day.

There's an excitement about using local transport in cities you don't know well, especially buses. You're never quite sure if you've caught the right bus, or where exactly it's going. That morning it was the driver who seemed to be uncertain about our route.

After we'd gone about a mile, the friendly chatter among the passengers suddenly subsided. Beth nudged me. 'This isn't the right way, we should have turned into Crown Street.' She stood up and called out to the driver. 'You've gone the wrong way.' The other passengers muttered in agreement. 'It's no good carrying on down this road, you need to get across to London Road,' Beth shouted. She moved up to the front of the bus and leant over the driver's shoulder. He was very young, and he was staring ahead helplessly, willing the road to turn into the one he should be on.

'Look, if you turn right down Great Newton Street, at the next corner, you'll get back onto the route,' Beth told him. 'I'll tell you where to go. You can trust me, you know.' She was sounding quite joky now, flirtatious even. The driver obediently turned at the next corner, hauling at the steering wheel to swing the bus into a very narrow street.

'Well, done. Keep going,' Beth said encouragingly as her pupil eased the bus between the pavements on either side. He looked nervous, and I couldn't blame him.

'Look,' said Beth, 'would you like me to take over? I've always longed to drive a bus and this is my one chance.'

By this time, several of the passengers had risen to their feet, like members of an audience; they were agog to see what happened next. No one seemed worried about missing bus stops. The driver grinned at Beth's suggestion and shook his head.

'Go on,' she said, 'let me.'

By this time he was laughing, with relief as much as anything else because we had almost reached the junction with the main road. As he swung the bus back onto the authorised route, Beth returned to her seat and the passengers clapped and cheered.

When we were getting off the bus, Beth asked the driver where he came from.

'Poland.' He grinned.

'I was thinking you weren't from around here,' she said.

Alan Williams   *My neighbour's ox*

Early in 1946 we moved into a newly built council house in Speke, a reward for my Dad having served as a rear gunner with RAF Bomber Command from 1940 and having against all the odds survived.

Plenty of opportunity to covet our neighbours' houses but not much point as they were all the same. Born in 1940 I was too young to covet our neighbour's wife but if I had been older she was such an unattractive, chain smoking, Guinness-soaked harridan, mother of innumerable children, I probably wouldn't have bothered.

The tenancy regulations forbade the keeping of livestock which did not deter some tenants from keeping pigs and hens in this post war period of austerity but not, as far as I can remember, oxen – and I was desperately interested in the idea of coveting an ox. The poor man living next door didn't own an ox but drank so heavily that he hallucinated at which time he would hold conversations in the back garden with an imaginary ox which I witnessed. This performance entranced me so much that I actually believed that the ox existed. I longed to possess it.

One day our poor neighbour suffered delirium tremens, he and his hallucinatory ox were taken away never to be seen again. When I confessed my sin to my priest he gave me absolution without penance on the grounds that he did not consider coveting somebody else's hallucination was even a venal never mind a mortal sin. Nor did he believe my desire to possess the ox had anything to do with the more usual biblical connotation of possession in view of my tender age. However he did give me a horrendous penance for wasting his time.

I went home, wrote a letter of resignation to the then Pope and have never been back to the church since or coveted an ox, real or imaginary.

You can only long for the unattainable. For most of a decade I yearned for an issue of a pulp magazine, and my first encounter with it was the seed of my writing career. I saw it in the window of a sweet shop in 1953, when it was common for such shops to sell magazines. The cover appeared to depict a bird-like creature cowering in terror of two monstrosities – huge human skulls for heads and very little in the way of bodies – approaching it across a black desert. If the cover looked like that, what extraordinary things would the magazine contain? At seven I wasn't allowed to find out, and so the image and the name of the publication – *Weird Tales* – haunted me for years.

Once I was ten my mother reluctantly relented, and I spent my pocket money for months on remaindered digest-sized fantasy and horror magazines dumped in cartons on the counter of a sweet shop in Old Swan and stamped sixpence a copy. I'd written my first published tale and was working on my first published book by the time I found the issue I'd been searching for. The cover shows a vulture perched on some bones with two admittedly evil-looking human skeletons in the background. It seems to me that back in 1953 my mind was already bent on improving on the terrors I encountered and rendering them more memorable. I've done so for the rest of my life.

Perhaps one dream was to write for the magazine. Of course that was impossible, since it folded in 1955, and so I could only write fiction that more modern issues might have published. Then it was revived, and a dream I wouldn't have dared indulge came true. The new editors didn't just buy my stuff, they published a special issue as a tribute. And yet – I don't mean this as any kind of ingratitude – the magic has somehow departed. Perhaps it needed unattainability of some kind to lend it power. Admittedly most of the contents of *Weird Tales* that deserve to be have been reprinted, but hardcovers don't smell of yellowed pulp, nor are they illustrated with that inimitable luridness. My collection of hundreds of issues has found a new home – the University of Liverpool's archives of the Science Fiction Foundation – and in a way I wish I missed them more. I yearn for my own yearning – for that lost 50s innocence where every magazine or book was an adventure, not to mention every bookshop (none more so than Bascombe's on Smithdown Road, a tobacconist's whose inner room was a trove of paperbacked fantasy). Of course there are still books that save me from becoming jaded, and the act of writing does. That's about longing if anything is – the longing to write what you never quite achieve. It's the reason you go on reaching for the next story, and the next. I'll be reaching for the rest of my life. Writers do.

Tayo Aluko   *The Royal wee*

I woke up with three feelings. First, the severe pain in my leg, where I've just had the operation. Second; relief that I'm obviously still alive. Third; I'm longing for a pee.

I look round the Royal Liverpool Hospital trauma ward. They're all still there: the 17-year-old who had an arm operation after an accident in Birkenhead; another broke his hip falling over drunk on Mathew Street; the old man from Huyton with tubes stuck into practically every orifice; and an

Intensive Care nurse who was himself rushed in with suspected spinal damage after falling over on Wood Street (the beer was 80p a bottle).

I pick up my urine bottle, position myself and wait. Nothing. I ignore the horrible noises from old man's chest, and drift back to sleep.

Next morning, the consultants and their entourages do their ward round. I notice they're all foreign. A beacon of multi-culturally progressive employment practices, I suggest to ICU nurse. He says it's simple economics: foreign staff will much more readily accept NHS wages, which amount to several times what they'd get at home, and foreign consult-ants generally arrive better educated than natives. Just then Teenager looks up from his *Nuts* magazine crossword and asks how to spell music.

My bladder's expanded. Teenager says his was the same: general anaesthetic sometimes has this effect, and he had to have a catheter. 'What's that?' I ask.

'They stick a tube up your willie into your bladder, and it emptys into this bag'.

'Sounds horrible. Does a male nurse do it?'

'Yes, not the fit babes, unfortunately.' I try again. Nothing.

I'm awoken at 4am by Teenager screaming from behind curtains. As his cries subside, three female nurses emerge, and disappear. He says they've just removed the catheter. I doubt he'll react favourably to pictures of sexy nurses in *Nuts* ever again.

Fit Nurse tells me I might have to be catheterised later, as it's been over 48 hours. I lose fluid, but through perspiration. She returns with the older, matronly one, who proffers the

12-inch contraption. I ask for one final try, and they draw the curtains around me.

After about thirty seconds, I let out an involuntary 'Oooooooaaaaaaahhhh!', as the bottle fills for what feels like five minutes, but remarkably runneth not over.

Fit Nurse fails to suppress a giggle as I hand her the bottle. I think I detect something in Matron's eye. Disappointment? No, I'm sure she shares my relief....

Liam Coàn   *Den wot?*

We spent a fair few 'ours ou'side in de daye light, unusu'lly warm n cloudless. Gives de city a romantik tinge, esp'es'elly bye St George's 'all. Go inside cos' d'eve got dis ting on 'bout de old marble flore. One ov dose tings your into or your knot. Te'll you wots a blinder dow, de way de city ahlways 'as its way. Now de te'll us wer different, well its ahlways bin lik dha. Luk a't de gold leef duor frames wid SPQL carved into 'em, an you'll see wot a mean.

Afder dha we 'ed up bold street onto concert square, ave

a few, ge't burn't, lobster-like; place is h'evin.

Den we retire to de flat on bold street n ave a game ov poker. Ten mins in an am on me arse bored outta me h'ed. A move to de window wid a bot'le ov wine. Dese drunks passé de trendie Oxfam, n stumble into de subway. An over me shoulder, on de o'dher side ov the flat, concert square gives way to n orgy of sound wid mischief mingled. A turn to de table as de o'dhers play; smokin', tossin chips into de fray. As mor ov dese little flat multi-colour'd disks tak de place ov clunky-litle-lumps-ov-metal. Down-stirs de city hums, n buzzes, woy-woy's n wolf whistles into de evening ir. I sit dere lik a sad-sak wid me bottle ov wine. Skin turning purple, smell lik frazzled pig. Ou'side or inside evrything eruptin. On the sidelines seat'd sighin.

Bastards.

Bronwyn Davis   *Another place*

When it gets too much I go to the beach at Crosby and stand among the statues. I follow their lead and stare out to sea, imagining going home, back to my family, my friends. I see in my mind's eye the streets I used to call home and the people I used to know.

Keeping in touch is much easier these days. Letters travel quickly, phone calls are cheap and there is also the internet. But sometimes I wish I could just be back there, not to do anything extraordinary, but just to spend time doing the everyday: shopping, sitting chatting, falling into companionable silence. The statues offer their own consolation, standing resolute regardless of the weather, facing away from these shores, facing towards home.

Diane Samuels   *Punch*

When I came home from infant school on my fifth birthday in 1965 there was a visitor waiting. Jumping excitedly in the hallway, he had a white coat blotched with brown. His tail was perky. He was a mongrel with a strong streak of terrier.

'He's your birthday present,' said mum.

'He's mine?' I couldn't believe that this living dog could be owned by anybody. I'd longed for my own pet. 'He's really mine?'

'His name's Punch.' Mum and dad had called him after the Punch & Judy, dad's cafeteria near Lime Street station. My grandad had wanted to bring a real-style American diner to the heart of Liverpool. He'd opened the place in the 1950s and it had become very popular. He'd called it after Codman's Punch and Judy show that played nearby at the turn of the century. So my mongrel had acquired a name with quite a heritage.

Punch was never trained. He tended to leap about like a demented Jack-in-the-box. When my friends came to play he would hurl himself at them. They would scream and run away in terror. He made a lot of noise but I don't remember him ever biting. He was a bundle of pure energy.

One day there was great excitement at my school, King David primary.

'There's a mad dog!'

A high-speed blur of fur was careering about the playgrounds and behind the kitchens. Then I saw my mum. She had come to catch him. It was Punch. Mum sent me back into class. She was seeing to it. I at once felt embarrassed and thrilled at the prospect of my pet hurtling into school. The children were whipping themselves into a frenzy. It was rumoured that he had rabies. A great drama was unfolding. Then mum appeared and told me that Punch was safely back on his lead. Shame. Relief.

A year later, when I was eight, we moved to Childwall Park Avenue. I returned home from tea at my friend's one afternoon to be told that something had happened. Mum had to repeat it three times, just as she had had to repeat that he was mine when I first found him in the hallway.

'Punch has been run over by a car.'

That was it. There was no sign of his body, ashes, a coffin, let alone a grave. He had just disappeared off the face of the earth.

'He was always running away. He never had any road-sense. He dashed out into Woolton Road. He had no chance, silly animal.'

This post-accident mantra was at once comforting and disturbing. It provided an explanation for the tragedy, making it understandable rather than random and terrifying. At the same time, it passed judgement – if you're wild then expect to be wasted. Punch was my free spirit in the domestic heartland. I loved him for that. Now he was gone. I couldn't believe it. I sobbed all night with his lead under my pillow.

Tom Riley   *The lonely sea and the sky*

I come from a long line of sailors: my father stoked the boilers of the old four-funnelled *Mauritania*. I was the spawn of a Walker's ale-house night ashore, and my blood ebbed and flowed in tune with the travelling moon and the night ships sang sweet songs to me in my rag-covered bed. I roamed unmolested around the magic domains of Derby Road, Regent Road, and all along the stony walls of the Canada and Brocklebank Docks.

Vivid pictures are still with me in my seventy ninth year: the great Clydesdales, straining with their loads of cotton bales and stamping fire from the cobbles, tossing their feedbags in the air to catch the last few oats, and sending the blinding fragments of bran and chopped straw flying in the wind. Their flowered splendour in the May Day processions and the all-pervading and invigorating smell of their dung.

The May Queens in their ragged finery; my promotion to gather the grubby white train of my queenly elder sister on a wet May Day and the subsequent sorrow as we were robbed by older children of our collection.

Bibby's steam lorries chuffing busily along the Dock Road: they would be unmanageable in today's traffic. The number 18 tram swaying and clanging along Derby Road, the gloved driver handling the imprecise controls like the conductor of a symphony orchestra.

Playing amongst the trains under the Docker's Umbrella, and my puny efforts to move the points lever; thank God it needed a fairly hefty adult to do that: we had no conception of the danger.

Most potent of all and unseen, the smells of romance tumbling over the forbidding walls of the docks: tobacco, molasses, tarred rope, oil-seed, steam and hot oil, seconded by the cries of the great ships as they manoeuvred in the river, in the serious business of making Liverpool great.

I was inoculated with longing, for the empty wave-bound horizon and the thin grey line of landfall. I thought these romantic leanings were snuffed out as in impotent rage I hammered my small fists on the great oak doors of Leyfield School in West Derby.

I was isolated from the real world for many years. The training I received, often brutal, in that place and another orphange, bred a resourceful and independent spirit. The seaman slumbered until the day when, in mid-channel, the whole strapping crew of our chartered yacht being incapable with sea-sickness, I was elected skipper and brought my ship safely into Cherbourg. I'm still sailing.

Lewis Biggs   *Bling it*

Bling lies at the heart of the Liverpool experience, always present, but reaching *maestro* level on a Friday night. Liverpool people just love attention. Not that we are greedy or needy, like those poor stage-actors who curl up and die if they think that they are being ignored for a minute. No, we just feel that a glance of appreciation or envy is as much the currency of conversation as verbal wit. Bling's the visual vocabulary of attitude, a kind of performance art. Within a group of people, it becomes a form of visual intercourse, the repartee of accessory. It's what I miss when I'm away.

Nicholas Allt   *Kiss and swim*

Two months from leaving, Degsy and I both hated maths at St Kevin's school, Kirkby. Logarithms, algebra and fractions – forget it! Thinking of joining the Merchant Navy due to a hankering for sea voyage, we'd bunk off each time a double lesson showed face; jumping the bus to the Pier Head to catch the ferry to New Brighton. After making the same backseat journey for a month or so we'd often bump into two fit girls, Angela and Paula from Queen Mary High, Norris Green. Up to the same antics, they apparently hated school full stop. Pairing up, me with Angela, Degsy with Paula, we hit it off immediately.

Now, if you hid inside the ferry toilets instead of disembarking on the Wirral side you could travel for free. It was an old Liverpool trick; one we performed so many times that the crew got used to seeing us, leaving us be. While the boat idled, dropping day tripping Scousers and homebound

Wirralians, stashed away in the ancient bogs we started necking the time away. On a beautiful, sunny May afternoon, a few days after Liverpool lifted the European Cup in Rome, my mate Degsy started performing pirate pirouettes and edge of the boat acrobatics, making out he was Emlyn Hughes hoisting his school bag/European Cup above his head. Paula and Angela laughed heartily, but Paula warned him 'One big wave and you're in!' Suddenly, somewhere midway between New Brighton and Liverpool a salty spray washed over us as a sudden wave hit portside. Enjoying the cold splash on sunburned cheeks, I cleared my eyes from slightly stinging salt water. Looking directly into sunrays I couldn't get Degsy into focus. Then I heard Angela 'He's over, he's bleedin' fell in!'

With heads craned over the side the three of us pointed wildly at a floating black jacket. Terrified, Angela ran screaming for the crew. Catching sight of Degsy, nowhere near his twisted school blazer, he was performing the breast stroke as if he was enjoying a cool afternoon dip on the French Riviera. Trailing in the ferry's wake, the foghorn sounded and we eventually came to a stop. Nonchalantly doggy paddling to the side of the boat, a crew member threw out a lifebelt and duly hoisted him up. With the girls shaken, him laughing and me gob-smacked, the captain and crew were livid. Back at the Pier Head landing stage they told him to wait for an ambulance. Seizing his chance, not wanting police intervention or his parents to find out, he ran off and I didn't see him till next day in school. Needless to say the two of us failed Maths O level miserably and Paula stopped seeing Degsy as she thought he was a nutter. I liked Angela's salty lips and carried on seeing her for a month or two. Although like a lot of Liverpool people we both loved the sea, neither of us joined the Merchant Navy.

Christopher George   *Beatles St Nicholas sonata*

It was a cool May stormy weather Mersey night following the tour I'd taken with Ged; his first guided tour of Beatles sites; John Lennon's secret wooded Woolton footpath, the sunlit field where the Quarrymen played fifty summers ago.

I brake the hired silver VW Passat on the road near Ged's Scottie Road housing estate, strip off the beige Ralph Lauren shirt he'd lent me. Aye! I am an exhibitionist on a midnight Scouse road. 'Ta ra, Ged mate, you done good, lad'.

I park outside my Pier Head hotel. A sudden screeching of seagulls peals out of the breezy night above St Nicholas's church steeple; a cloud of white wings against black sky above the illuminated lantern of sculpted Gothic arches, gold sailing ship shining at the pinnacle.

One of the final tasks of the year on the allotment was to tidy up all the dead vegetation and burn it on the bonfire. I loved the smell of that fire. If I smell a bonfire nowadays it still reminds me of the allotment, and all the hours we spent there which was well worth the effort when you were tucking into new potatoes and fresh garden peas.

As the colder weather was starting to set in, and money was always scarce, if the coal stocks were getting low before the coalman called again, I was sent down to Garston with a large battered old green bag. This was the Coal Brick Bag. You could, for 1/9d buy a coal brick, which was about the size of a house brick, and it had a groove across the middle so that you could break it in half. I was told to buy six of these bricks each time I had to go. Being a slightly built (skinny) child, you can imagine how difficult it was to carry this bag of coal bricks for about a mile and a half. But you didn't complain, you went and got them, and when you got home mum would have a hot cup of tea ready for you and you would sit by the fire she had made with one of these bricks, which by the way gave out tremendous heat, and curl up with your comics.

As the mornings took longer to get light, I can remember a man would walk up our long road and pull on the chains at the side of the street lights to turn them off, and in the early evening he would do the same job again, only in reverse, to turn them on again. Sometime in the mid sixties, the Corpy put new lights up, which came on all by themselves. I often wondered what happened to the street lamp man after those modern lights were put in.

Ranulph Fiennes   *Nirvana in the North*

Brought up in South Africa and Sussex, army years in Germany and Arabia, worked in London, settled on Exmoor, and now over 60, I've clearly missed out on the wonders of Liverpool. But my ancestor Celia Fiennes, the daughter of a top Cromwellian general, was a famous travel writer, and back in 1698 described 'Leverpoole' as 'London in miniature as much as ever I saw any thing.'

Twenty years ago my late wife's little sister Abby moved from the deep South East (Sussex) to the northern fastness (Liverpool) on a whim. We all prayed for her well-being. I knew that the Beatles had come from up there and I could even croon most of the words of *Ferry Cross the Mersey*. The place from which came Scousers was somewhere up by Manchester and Blackpool.

This, my dreadful state of ignorance, quickly changed when Abby began to send highly positive reports back south about her new home in Aigburth. The local folk were warm, sincere and welcoming, even to Sussex toffs, the town was knee deep in history and culture (and not just Fab Four stuff), traffic jams and pollution were nowhere in evidence and,  best of all, Abby's new job was proving a great success.

In a while Abby's mother, my much loved mother-in-law of some 30 years, also moved to this Nirvana-in-the-North, where she settled in a cosy dockside apartment. Visiting her, I finally got to see Liverpool, soon to be Europe's Capital of

Culture, and I have to agree with my ancestor Celia. Although her comment that 'tho there be 24 streetes in it' may no longer be true, her observation that Liverpool is 'grown to a large fine town' can't be argued with.

Catherine Sparks   *Walt Disney ferry*

As a child, the pull of the river took me to the Pier Head with my friends. I grew up in Huyton, so we would take the bus to town. We hardly ever got off before the Pier Head, why would you? You have to get to the very edge, the defining line.

The ferry was fun when I was young; a bit grey and grim, a bit 1970s, a bit black and white. But I sat on the deck and smelt the sea, got tats in my hair as the wind blew and tasted salt on my lips. And no-one sang to me from cheap speakers to tell me just what experience I was having and what I should be feeling.

It was my ferry 'cross the Mersey.

Matt Simpson   *Mixing memory and desire*

Longing, like the Liver Birds, looks both backwards and forwards – it is that mixing of memory and desire T S Eliot writes about in *The Waste Land*. It lives between absence and fulfilment, between something missed and something to be gained or regained. For sea-going men it's the ship between ports; for the women it's waiting for their men and their pay packets to return to port. Liverpool has had centuries' experience of it; it's ingrained.

It has always been a place of arrivals and departures. It breeds a stoic philosophy of come-day, go-day, sans-faire-rien. It also breeds nostalgia. Every Scouser that leaves the city takes with them a feeling of exile and a peculiar kind of loyalty. Like heroes in hero myths, they have a tendency to come back. It's a rhythm: the ebb and flow of the river and of the sea itself. Scousers have brine in their veins. Or is this just me being nostalgic?

Beneath whatever hard exteriors they pretend to, Scousers are invariably soft-hearted to the point of sentimentality. They love and miss 'the good old days'. *Yesterday all my troubles seemed so far away.* It's the 'days thee useter woz' – when the docks were bustling with cargo boats and liners, there were the Overhead Railway, Blacklers, Owen Owens, the old St John's Market with the shawlies selling sticks of celery, Tommy Handley, Arthur Askey, Ted Ray, and all those fine boxers that came out of the city. It is said you have to be a comedian to live in Liverpool or a boxer to fight your way out of it. Maybe it's ambivalence, the friction between opposites, which turns us into jokers. Most Liverpool jokes are of the debunking variety: set something up to knock it down.

Nostalgia and hope go together. Buddhists see this as attachment to the past through memory and to the future through desire. It's something they try to escape from. But not Liverpudlians. The city's two cathedrals, pointing heavenwards (the Catholic one sometimes colloquially called the Pope's Rocket) are connected by a street called

Hope – which also houses the Everyman Theatre, the Philharmonic Hall and the wonderful Philharmonic pub. Scousers look forward: to returning home, to getting back to sea, to the next pint, the match on 'satdee'. Pride in the past helps them to project futures: re-emergence from the Blitz, celebrating 800 years, becoming the Capital of Culture, winning the Cup, the League, going out the weekend for a few bevvies. The statue by Epstein over the portals of Lewis's deparatment store is entitled *Liverpool Resurgent*. It too now has to carry ambivalence.

The city is constantly changing. Between the demolishing of the old and the construction of the new there will always and inevitably be space for longing.

Gill McEvoy   *His and hers*

There are great concrete buttresses at my back holding up a lantern of light. I call this street the His and Hers. I'm sitting on concrete steps – not a blade of leaf, a hint of green anywhere but for one resilient dandelion working its way through a crack. Little survivor. I come here for the huge sky: tall river-meets-sea light, gulls wheeling and screaming, silvering the air, and the smell of all those far-off places I've never been to, swept briskly up here by the winds off the Mersey. Close your eyes, you could be anywhere. It's magic.

I'm sitting by His. Hers − or mine − is at the other end. Hope Street they call it. Mixed marriages never work, they said, tutting all those years ago. But we were sure it would. We had hope. So cocksure. I never converted and he was lapsed − until the end when he shot from my arms like a rabbit and fled into the arms of His. Leaving me facing a widowhood stranger and harsher than that caused by death. He did die, of course. In the end the disease got him. I felt so excluded then, couldn't even read his favourite poem by the graveside at the interment.

But time passes. You creep out of the cracks again, go on.

On wet days I sit inside. Yes, in His. I love the light. 'Where there's light there's hope', they say, or something like that. In Hope Street hope is what I cling to.

Nigel Malpass   *Dockology*

It was a bright Saturday afternoon in early 1964 as we lay alongside the Bibby Henderson berth in Birkenhead and as midshipmen living in the half deck we were all taking a well-earned siesta. We lived in the after deck housing on the boat deck, six to a cabin and next to the ship's hospital. A bit cramped by modern standards and essential that you remembered to close the collapsible canvas washbasin before opening the door. There was, however, much merit living in such a remote part of the ship as by this means we escaped the ever-watchful eye of the Chief Officer.

Of course the downside to this arrangement was the fact

that two of the cargo steam winches were situated directly overhead and whilst working cargo it was like living in a railway tunnel with the *Flying Scotsman* passing through. This particular Saturday was very quiet as the ship lay alongside having finished discharging the inbound cargo the previous day. It would be Monday before we commenced loading, and ten days before the passengers embarked prior to our departure for Rangoon. Imagine our surprise when we were suddenly disturbed by a loud knocking on our doors only to find that the Chief Officer was in the alleyway. The only time he would normally appear in our accommodation was on a Saturday morning when 'the march of the unemployed looked at the unemployable' better known as the Master's weekly cabin inspection.

It quickly became apparent that two men in brown overalls had turned up driving a flat top lorry with a requisition form signed by the company's senior superintendent. This required that the grand piano be landed for overhaul and tuning. The piano was situated in the passenger lounge forward of number three hatch, so without more to do the senior cadet was ordered to arrange for its removal.

Not a problem for twelve cadets, and we soon had it out of the lounge via the french doors and up on to the starboard side of the boat deck. Using the ship's derricks and a system of spreaders the piano was secured protecting it where necessary by the use of spare pillows obtained from the Purser. It was an easy matter for the lorry to be reversed so that the flat top was directly under the piano as it was lowered over the side, and within half an hour of the workmen's arrival it was in place, secured and ready to travel. All the necessary papers were signed with a copy kept for the ship's files. As we climbed the gangway, the driver shouted up that they should be back by Thursday.

That was the last time anyone saw either the piano, the lorry or the two men that collected it. I subsequently learned that this technique was known locally as applied dockology.

Will Alsop   *City of dreams*

A city has to believe in itself in order to be belligerent and edgy – Liverpool has a heady mix of awkwardness and

attitude, which makes for an exciting place. This former departure place for many people seeking the new world combined with its prominence as an Irish city has always led to a city of uncertainty, even when it had the self confidence, that comes with wealth, to challenge London as the jewel in the English crown. The city was always stealing from others; it developed its own ceramics as a challenge to Stoke, whose products Liverpool was exporting. This resulted in a lost inheritance that manifested itself through grand civic buildings alongside poverty and the nervousness of the émigrés. This city of contradictions contradicts itself. It never quite believes that it can be what it wants to be.

We all love and hate Liverpool, but secretly we all long for the city to achieve a greatness that is occasionally tender.

Michèle McGrath
The Beatles are coming

'The Beatles are coming to America!'

I raised my head, stunned. Could it possibly be the same group I had known in Liverpool? Louise was waving a newspaper picture. There they were, twelve thousand miles from home. In an instant, the palm trees and sunshine faded and I was back in the crowded smoky atmosphere of the Cavern, laughing and chatting with a group of boys that I had never expected to see again. I did not know it then, but I was one of the lucky ones. For a year, I had spent every Saturday night at the Cavern and most of the lunchtimes too. I took my O levels that year and we went to the Picton Library to study, in our dreadful school uniform. We did study, but not at lunchtime, that was our time to dance. We would take off our ties, roll up the sleeves of our blouses, hike up our horrible skirts as short as possible and pull out stilettos and lipstick from our schoolbags.

We tottered our way across town and down the rickety wooden staircase, into a room thronged with people and filled with throbbing music. The floor was uneven and it was easy to break a heel off your shoe or twirl, stagger and run your heel down someone's leg, making it bleed. The toilets were disgusting and you could not see across the room for the smoke. If a fire had started we would never have got out. But it never did.

There were small benches and tables on the right, as you looked towards the stage. They were always filled with necking couples. Most of the girls hoped to spend at least part of the time on those benches and it was fun to be asked, but I used to stay close to the stage, listening to the music and chatting with the bands.

I heard all the groups, Gerry and the Pacemakers and the Merseybeats amongst others, but the Beatles were my favourites. I loved John's wit. He could cap anything anyone said to him and make everyone laugh. Paul knew he was good looking and strutted around. I thought he was bigheaded. George was shy and stayed in the background. But their drummer was Pete Best. There were no suits and trademark haircuts then, only black leather and rumpled hair. Their first local hit was *My Bonnie*. I bought a copy and it had travelled with me to California, a prized possession.

'Michèle, wake up! What are you thinking about?'

'I was thinking about home.' I said dreamily, 'and a group of boys I once knew'.

Catherine Peters   *La vie en rose*

Tongue twisters en route to childhood eye tests in Rodney Street. *I chased a pup up Upper Parliament Street.* At twelve years old, I learnt in Mr Benedict-Smith's cabinet of optical curiosities that I'd inherited not just my father's love of language but the family myopia. Less daunting thanks to Lennon, a bespectacled fate loomed large, if a little blurry.

My sight was failing but not before those same streets had opened my eyes to their cinematic beauty, their distinction and their grace. A film set for a childhood with a charismatic cast.

And two decades on, as we visit our mother in an eighth floor hospital room, we pass an ophthalmic roll of honour which includes our esteemed optician and his father too – the Benedict-Smiths I and II. Credits well deserved seen through four eyes they had preserved.

In all that time, I've pursued la vie en rose. I've seen reds, whites and blues in Oxford, France and London. But, in truth, life's never been so rosy as when the NHS dispensed pink, plastic frames to little girls like me, laughing as we tripped on words.

Terence Davies   *Down all the days*

There I sat.
And there I wept.
There my heart was full.

But you – who do not share an older past – cannot know that killing of the soul which is regret, cannot know the longing that lies deep inside the heart.

The taxi slides through town and my old senses rise to remember the Majestic there, the Gaumont there or some other long-since-gone remembrance of the days gone by.

There was old St John's Market crowded with vegetables

and women selling fruit and where my brother Tony bought a dog for my brother Kevin... who called it Rex.

There the small café (opposite the Forum) where waitresses in black and white served tea on silver trays or Sampson and Barlow in London Road where 'functions' took place for those who could afford them; or else there was the Kardomah or Lyons for those who could not.

And the smooth purr of the escalators at Owen Owens during the summer holidays.

And you, who are young, who do not remember when George Henry Lees was once so exclusive no-one entered the shop, or the Bon Marché in brown and cream livery, or when Stoniers was once the Gucci of glassware... you who are young – where all is democratic, where there is no hierarchy of taste will walk past those stores (and the ones that are no more) and will never know the exotic smell of coffee being roasted at Coopers near Paradise Street.

Perhaps it is best you do not remember or regret or have a longing so deep it hurts the soul... for you there may not be that sad enjoyment... well, perhaps not yet... but in fifty years time as your grandchildren point to something new you, too, may say 'It was different in my day' or 'Things are not the same now' and you, too, may remember the small ecstasy of going into town to buy something special for the kids at Christmas.

So do not wail.

So do not curse the happiness of the passing hour.

Hold it in your heart and (at some *very* distant, future date) unwrap it in the quiet of a room and say – with wonder – 'Oh! This is how it was!'

Szilvia Opavszki   *Five senses*

Trying to escape from my everyday routine I suddenly find myself in Albert Dock – bright sunshine, pure colours and sharp contrasts. The sky is a never reachable ceiling, and the water surface is the ballroom floor for the light wind. Behind the redbrick walls and mysterious arches sits the Liver Building with the two majestic birds.

How could I forget this ceremonious and peaceful corner of the world? The longer I stay the more details I notice.

Hidden behind the seagulls' cries I can hear the delicate splashes of the water. The wind whispers distant sounds of city traffic in my ears. A woman is laughing somewhere.

It is good to be back again.

I lean against a wall and close my eyes. It is blowing up for rain with a refreshing smell. When the first sobering raindrops land on my face I take a last look.

Then, smiling, I slowly close my photo album.

Tony Lane *Seaman finds Liverpool and gets converted*

It was a cold, grey late January morning in 1956 when I first arrived in Liverpool at the end of my first voyage as an apprentice deck officer. We'd been away for six months when we took a line from a coal-burning tug throwing out windswept balls of black smoke. I was 18 years old. Late that afternoon I got ashore and straight onto the Overhead. It was truly amazing. Five miles of ships, variously exotic and nauseous smells – molasses, coffee beans, tropical timbers, wet hides, bales of cotton – confirmed my membership of the seafaring trade. My first stop was a small chemists in

Dale Street to hand in a film from my Brownie for developing and printing. A very attractive girl of about my age served me and impulsively I asked her out. She accepted. We went to the pictures. I saw her onto her bus home. Next day we sailed for a London pay-off and I never saw her again. More confirmation of the life of a seaman and it was all happening in Liverpool. What a wonderful place, I thought. This was not a very original thought, I later discovered when talking to other seamen, past and present. I may have been born in Gosport and spent my teenage years in the Isle of Wight but when I became a seaman I was reborn into a universal community where place of origin came second to being a shipmate.

Four years later I married a Liverpool girl. Marriage signalled the end of most sea careers and it did mine. Academic life came next. Specialising in industrial relations and the labour movement quickly brought me into close and continuous contact with the then much-reviled shop stewards and political activists. I was enormously impressed with the integrity and commitment of many of them and this led me to dig ever deeper into the lives of Liverpool's people. I was led into places that told me decisively that this was a city of the sea. Since my retirement in 2003 I have continued to write about seamen who are, more than any other workers, citizens of the world first and of nations second. I learned this in Liverpool, too.

Christine Webb   *Liverpool Cathedral bells*

I've 'grabbed' any number of cathedrals from Edinburgh to Truro, toiling up endless stone stairs, edging across walkways high above the nave to reach the ringing chamber. But not Liverpool. Liverpool is unique with its two lifts to take you to the huge ringing chamber where the rope circle falls in just one part of it. Its magnificent bells are the heaviest ring of twelve in the country. I can only imagine the glorious sound pealing across the city. I haven't rung them yet, but I will, and it will be a joy and a privilege.

Niall Griffiths   *Birthday card from Ward B-4*

Hello Eddie – and happy birthday – bet you thought I'd forget! You're 35 now, am I right? Or about 35, anyway. It's been three years since I last saw you and I remember your 32nd cos I bought you them rocks off that feller everyone called Starfish, remember? Cos he had one tattooed on his neck. And then we bought the other stuff off him to bring us down and I ended up in hospital and that's how you spent your 32nd birthday, at my side wondering if I would die, do you remember, Eddie? I do. Remember it, I mean. Funny how you can forget things the day after but remember them years later, isn't it? I'd like to be there today to see you getting older,

Eddie, and see what's happened to you in the past few years and if there's any white in your beard or hair. Or even if you've still got a beard. Or hair!!! Mine has grown back now after I shaved it all off (my hair, I mean, not my beard!) a couple of months ago just before they brought me in here. And the skin on my arm has grown back, too. I haven't had a drink in two months, can you believe that, Eddie? Me! And I haven't touched anything else for nearly a year but I was getting bad on the vodka for a bit. Melanie, d'you remember her? Had red hair and shared a flat in Lark Lane with Declan? Well, she died the week before I came in here. The doctor said that her heart and liver were working 5,000 times harder than a normal person's and that's what killed her and I went to see her in hospital and she was yellow Eddie. Bright yellow. She'd only been out of detox a week. That won't happen to me, tho – I'm staying off it when I get out, honest to God I am. I want to stay alive now. I'd like to see you when I get out but I bet you're still with Marianne and she won't let you see me and if you don't want to either that's okay. There's nothing I can do about that. But I still miss you and I miss those days when there was only us.

Happy birthday to you Eddie
Your friend (sober!!!)

Philip Ferguson · *Longing for Liverpool*

I am sitting here, nowhere to go. It's 7 o'clock pm and I've only my thoughts for company, longing for the day I can walk my three Jack Russell terriers along the beach and gaze upon that majestic waterfront across the Mersey. Night time being my fave, as the Liverbirds seem to come alive, when they are illuminated.

My thoughts are so vivid I can almost smell the salt air, this will keep me going for a while. It's a great thing the mind in HMP Liverpool.

Margo McDonough *The history of the dance halls*

Most couples aged 60 or 70 and over met at the local dance hall. One of these matchmaking love nests was the Grafton Ballroom.

The Grafton was built for the sole purpose of dancing with a sprung floor. It had a marble stairway and an arched roof. Many well known orchestras played there: Mrs Wilf Hamer, Victor Sylvester, Duke Ellington and Joe Loss. It was built on the site of a fairground next to that other famous venue: the Locarno, or the 'Lock'.

The Second World War meant a shortage of men, so girls would dance together, a fashion that is still customary today. One night a bomb dropped in the alley between the Grafton and the Locarno. Everybody looked up to see the ceiling full of holes. Mrs Wilf Hamer was playing the piano at the time, and she carried on playing till the All Clear started.

The Locarno was formerly named the Liverpool Olympia and was opened in 1905. It is a Grade II listed building modelled on the Kirov Ballet in Moscow. Because most department stores closed on a Wednesday afternoon there was always a dance at the Locarno. It was usual for stores to be allocated free tickets for a few lucky shop assistants. I used to work in T J Hughes and remember snuggling up to the boy from the soft furniture department in a slow foxtrot. How I long to see that rotating spinning ball emitting an ultra-violet light, the one that made all the fellows' white shirts glow. Mohair suits with a slim Jim tie was the fashion in the fifties. There was a strict rule that men had to wear ties. Many an eager young dancer was turned away, although it was possible to borrow a tie from the bouncer on the door.

For reasons which are hard to understand, the clientele who frequented the Grafton were always considered more upmarket than than those of the neighbouring dance hall. Perhaps they were over twenty one, whereas at the Lock teenagers would slyly jive in the corner near to the band, hoping they were not discovered. There was a huge notice on the wall warning dancers: NO JIVING. In 1963 a lesser-known group played to an audience of 200 and were paid £45 – now famously known as The Beatles.

Of course this was all very well but what if you could not dance? The place to learn was Billy Martin's of Derby Lane, a name well known during the 1940s. The dancing school opened on 5th December 1937. Billy was married to Pauline who carried on running classes on her own during the war while Billy was fighting for his country.

In 2004 eighty years of dancing was celebrated when the Grafton staged a big get-together. The memories came flooding back for all the 60, 70 and 80 year olds. What a wonderful night for the dancers as they relived their halcyon days at this special celebration.

The port of Liverpool was the great revolving door of nineteenth century Europe, spinning faster and faster. Raw materials like cotton rushed in to feed the mills of industrial England and a flood tide of humanity washed out to fill the cities, and populate the empty spaces of America and Australia. Nine million Irish, Russians, Poles, Jews, Germans, Swedes, Norwegians and others arrived in Liverpool and bewilderedly searched for a ship to take them across the Atlantic or halfway round the world. For all but the few rich, the trip – five weeks to America, ten or more to Australia before steam – was dirty, crowded and uncomfortable with a potentially bright but dreadfully uncertain life at the end. Why did they do it? Longing looks forward as well as back, framing hope as well as nostalgia. Did they miss the food, the smells, the language of their farms, market towns, hamlets and ghettoes? Of course they did. But more powerful than homesickness were their dreams of opportunity and freedom, often betrayed, if only in the short term, by the poverty and discrimination that waited for them in their new worlds. Many passed through Ellis Island in New York where, from 1903, Emma Lazarus' poem greeted them: 'Give me your tired, your poor, Your huddled masses yearning to breathe free.' Few turned back. Fortunately though, enough stayed behind to change the face of Liverpool. As *The Buildings of England* notes 'The unusual diversity of Victorian Liverpool's population is expressed in three tremendously un-English religious buildings' and goes on to cite Princes Road Synagogue, the Greek Orthodox Church of St Nicholas and the Swedish Seamen's Church. Like the Chinese arch on

Nelson Street, these buildings, these exotic visitors to an English townscape, are all architectural expressions of longing: longing for the familiarity of respective old countries and longing to be part of a bright future in the great port city.

John Thackray   *Judas's couch*

It was early one Good Friday morning. I was awake and excited at the prospect of going to the bonfire that the older boys had built to burn an effigy of Judas. This was not a popular activity with the fire bobbies or the 'scuffers', and boys my age – I was 5 years old in 1956 – were not usually welcome at such events.

In my dad's opinion this was not a suitable activity for young men to engage in and especially if their father worked in George Henry Lees. He was at the front door, intent on keeping guard, and I was resigned to my fate of seeing only the ash and dying embers of this fire later that morning.

Disappointed, I headed for my bedroom, when I heard voices at our front door. I stopped and hid behind the banisters. It was Sammy Doyle and Walter Bateman and a couple of others. What could they possibly want? My heart leapt for a moment thinking they had come for me.

Soon they were in our parlour where Joney used to live. (Joney was an elderly lady with a single room for which my dad didn't charge her rent. He was a good man). They were taking her old couch to the bonfire. I felt a sense of pride at making such a major contribution.

We lived in Park Street in the Dingle, and the secret location of the bommy was a jigger in Essex Street – near enough to carry an old couch to. Soon they were around the corner and gone. Now those who know this area will wonder at the wisdom of having a bonfire in Essex Street, as this was the location of both a fire station and a police station.

I retired to my bedroom to watch and sulk, but I was soon intrigued by the appearance of two scuffers, Sammy, Walter, the two others and of course the couch. I returned quietly to my hiding place.

The scuffers asked if this was our couch and said that they had apprehended these so-and-sos taking this couch to a bommy and that you had given it to them. Dad reluctantly corroborated their story. The sergeant then said that he would like dad to accept ten shillings in payment for the couch as it was in far better condition than the one at the station. They were looking out for a replacement and this one would do nicely.

He then politely stuffed a ten bob note into my dad's hand, shut his gaping lower jaw and with a cheery good morning told the boys to take the couch to Essex Street Police Station and exchange it for the one in the station which could go onto the bommy... and to be quick about it as they'll have to tell the fire bobbies about the bommy but not until they'd burned the old one – WELL GET GOING!

David Pearce   *Lunchtime longing, Liverpool*

I want to see the sunlight flicker on the ripples as the tide
flows in; I watch the screens that flicker round the edges of
the room. I want to hear the gulls mewling, wheeling across
lapping waves; I listen to the phones and voices round the
room. I want to stroll along the bank and see the rushing
water wash away the tracks across the sand; I walk beside the
kerb and watch the traffic crawling past. I want to sense the
cold and freshness of the breeze that blows in from the sea;
I feel the heat from engines throbbing as they wait. I want to
taste the subtle salt, caressing my nose and mouth; I imbibe
the fumes that catch my throat and prick my eyes. I want to
stand, and walk away, down the Mersey, down to the sea; I
sit under the clock that regulates our lives and know there
is not time enough.

Ted Jones   *Dixie Dean*

My brothers and I always knew when we were going to visit
Uncle Tom, because Dad would make us put on the blue and
white striped ties which were kept in the sideboard drawer
for that sole purpose. Uncle Tom was a Liverpool supporter.

In another drawer was a huge rattle that I could barely lift,
let alone turn, festooned with blue and white ribbons. Like
the fading rosette, it was a souvenir of Dad's greatest moment:
his trip to Wembley in 1933 to see Everton win the FA Cup.

Everton's star at the time was a centre forward – we didn't
call them strikers in those days – called William Ralph Dean.
If Everton was our religion, Dixie Dean was its high priest.
Dixie was a goal-scoring genius, less famed for dribbling

finesse than for raw courage, skill in the air and instinctive positioning.

The earliest reading matter I can remember were crumpled clips from the *Liverpool Echo* recording Dixie's greatest performance, in the 1927-28 season, when at the age of 21, he scored more League goals in a season than anyone before or since, taking Everton to the League Championship in the process. A football great, who, at the peak of his incredible career, earned £8 a week.

Matthew Williams   *Different river*

Right at the bottom of St Vincent Road, Wallasey, there's a gap in the houses, revealing a wonderful view across the River Mersey. Twenty one years ago, my girlfriend had her home there, and on foggy nights we'd sit on her garden wall and watch, through the mists, a red warning buoy blink rhythmically out over the dark waters. And with that light came the strange, melancholy call of the fog siren – *whooooooo... boop, boop, boop...* and we'd snuggle up together in the cold, whispering that the Loch Ness Monster had swum down from Scotland especially to wink and whistle at us, kissing in the dark. Safe and warm in each other's arms, the riverside fog wove a blanket around us, hiding us away from human eyes.

We were seventeen, and thought True Love lasted for ever. We had no idea how soon it would all end, and why. Mercifully, perhaps, our futures were concealed from us. One day I hope to go back to that garden and look out across the river, to see if the Loch Ness Monster still visits. Perhaps he's been calling to us these long years, mourning our absence. I hope he will remember me, alone.

They say you can never step into the same river twice – once the waters have gone, they will never return. I believe it, though I wish, I wish, it were not true.

Thomas Norton   *Waiting for Uncle Jack*

When Uncle Jack returned from one of his long voyages he would always spend his leave (and his fat pay-packet) on taking me out. Oh! how a young lad, living in a flat near Birkenhead docks, so looked forward to those trips around Merseyside.

I suppose for my seafaring uncle most of those nautical outings were a sort of busman's holiday – but for me they satisfied a boyhood passion for the sea and ships.

Sometimes it was along the promenade from Seacombe Ferry to New Brighton where we'd watch one-legged Pete dive off the pier – and I'd be slipped a couple of bob to spend in the Tower Fairground.

That was usually followed by a sail on the ferry boat across Mersey where I could watch great liners berthing at the landing stage – then back to Birkenhead where I could see the famous shipyard where they were being built. Or, at other times, I'd be taken along the long line Liverpool docks on the old Overhead Railway until I knew the name of every dock from Garston to Seaforth.

But it wasn't always about ships: sometimes my sailor uncle liked to enjoy a change – and where better than Merseyside for that? How well I can remember those train trips to Southport. Always a stop-off to see the red squirrels in Formby woods with the usual lemonade in Lord Street and a row on the boating lake. Neither can I forget boarding a Green Goddess at the Pier Head bound for Anfield or Goodison Park and being taken round those cultural wonders in William Brown Street.

Oh, how great it was for a ship-bound sailor and a downtown boy to be able to walk through the glorious green countryside and wander along the sandy beaches of our own Wirral peninsula.

Then it happened. One Autumn day, I read in *The Daily Post* shipping news that Uncle Jack's ship had gone, 'For extensive repairs into dry-dock at Karachi.'

Karachi! the name of that wretched port still seems to be engraved on my heart. It was certainly the prelude to the worst period of my young life: the joys of Christmas came and went and the following spring arrived without a sign of Uncle Jack.

No wonder I was pining away. Never a day passed when I didn't pester my poor Mam with the same question: 'When will Uncle Jack be back?' and never a night went by when I didn't lie awake longing for a certain Blue Funnel Boat to come sailing up the Mersey.

But that awful anguish continued, until one morning during the following summer holidays, I heard familiar footsteps on stone floors. Then, the merest glimpse of a weather beaten face passing our kitchen window changed everything: all those dreadful months of longing suddenly dissolved in a moment of sheer bliss.

Joanne Benford   *Dreams*

In an untamed corner of St John's Gardens, a newspaper flutters in the breeze, sunning itself in peaceful oblivion. On the back page next to the comics, above the Super crossword, the advertisement shouts LET US MAKE YOUR WILDEST DREAMS COME TRUE. A scrap is torn off and freed. It floats away across the park. Dreams, it says. Just the one word. Dreams. Gliding over the rubbish, the empty bottles, crumbling leaves of the peace gardens. Dreams, says the paper, unsullied by what it passes. Our dreams dance daintily over the world borne by the breezes of life and chance. Dreams know no limits. They journey. Glorious light and happy ever afters. I am held in its spell. A boy screams through the park, sinking the paper into the mud. In a small brown puddle, it drowns. The magic palace smashed, made of nothing but dreams.

Roger Phillips   *Through the tunnel*

I know you should never look backwards, but there are times... times when you hear a particular noise, smell a certain odour, get that sudden flash of déja vu. It's not in your control; it just appears in your mind. The buzzing of bees can take me back to a lazy summer afternoon, lying on the grass in Grange-over-Sands. There's sometimes a tang in the air that connects me to memories of a one special day in Keswick, when I bought my first (plastic!) teddy bear on my own at the age of six.

But living as I now do in Liverpool, there are memories I simply can't avoid. You see, when I was a child, we lived in Manchester – and a trip to Liverpool was a very special day out for the family. As I drive along the Dock Road, or through the Birkenhead tunnel, it sometimes feels as if I'm 50 years younger – seeing all the ships unloading, the trams, the hustle and bustle, sometimes the fog; and through the tunnel, I remember that feeling – would the sea break through, how would we escape?

And then, for a few moments, I long for that time of innocence. When it was summer for months, when winter knew its place and brought snow and fun; when it was always spring in April; and the glorious colours of autumn seemed to last for ever.

Was it ever like that? I don't really know – but, at times, I do long for it.

Karoline Fritzsch   *A Beatles story*

When I was eight years old, I discovered my dad's Beatles album. In order to sing along. I started writing down the lyrics, and as I didn't speak a word of English, I ended up with pages full of words that didn't exist in any language, but sounded right. At 25, I still catch myself discovering the real lyrics.

When I was thirteen years old, I was a full-blown Beatles fan. I decided to go on a pilgrimage and cycle all the way from eastern Germany to Liverpool, a plan that I never realised and laughed at as I got older. At 25, I'm settled in the city that seems to have been with me all this time.

Mysterious ways, indeed.

Gill Torres   *Nan in the flat*

As a child Liverpool meant grandparents; hot chocolate, old hands, wise voices, staying up too late and looking out of that window.

That window on the tenth floor at the top of the city. On a clear day you could see the Welsh mountains but at night before bedtime when the sky was black, that's when the city sparkled. The world transformed into a sea of stars below me as I sat, suspended in my bubble in the sky, knowing that all of life was happening down there. A thousand Saturday nights out rose like a haze and filled me with sweet longings as I drifted off to sleep.

This morning I woke up there; beneath the stars and the streetlamps with a hangover, an empty pizza box and the smug knowledge that it's every bit as good as I'd expected.

Just sometimes I look up to the top of the city I used to know, with a nod to Paddy's Market mornings and Nan's corned-beef hash. As I wipe away last night's make-up those innocent Saturdays seem to float away from me, like a bubble on the breeze.

Mathew Capper   *Oh Liverpool, oh life*

Wylie wrote 'heart as big as the city', and Jimmy Osmond sang about his 'long haired lover'. For me e e cummings is more relevant when he said 'one look will easily unclose me'. He wasn't talking about Liverpool, he was talking about love, and it's love I have for this fabulous city. Like any lover it has its problems and little blemishes, but in a strange way it's those blemishes that make me love and care for it even more.

No-one wants to see kids killing kids or a scourge of drugs. But when we love no-one wants to argue or fall out. The important thing is that I can forgive any blemishes and cherish every moment I have in our proud walls.

I live and belong here. I often leave and visit paradise in the Lake District or the mountains of Wales, but every time I return I feel safe once again knowing I've come back home to where I belong, because I belong in Liverpool, in Toxteth to be precise. I do not know what it is about Liverpool that closes and opens, only something in me understands the voice of its streets are deeper than all roses, its splendour touches skilfully, majestically. I know I cannot live without it, like oxygen I need it. Oh Liverpool, oh life.

Jeanette Smith   *Playing by the Mersey*

Growing up on the Waterloo shore, life revolved around the nearby beach. Hot summer days were spent digging in the sand, making burrows, where we would all shelter and giggle – not knowing the danger of the roof falling in. We would drag metal lorry tracks, used for sand winning to build post-war homes for returning soldiers, to cover our dug-out dens, and then throw over more sand and marram grass to make the perfect hideaway – safe from the gang from the next street. Until they discovered us, ran over the roof and we all scrambled, shrieking, to safety.

Mothers in slacks and permed hair would bring down plastic boxes full of jam sandwiches and home-made lemonade which we would devour hungrily – exhausted by our play. The odd bit of sand in the sandwiches was normal, the gritty mouthfuls scraping our teeth. We would even have competitions to see how much sand we could eat, while our less daring friends pulled distasteful faces.

And then there were the black oil slicks. These would be put into cream soda bottles, capped and set alight. We felt indestructible as they exploded, glass flying skywards.

Living on the shore meant that we quickly learned where the sinking sand lay. This brought great excitement as we plunged our tanned, bare limbs deep into the squelchy, sucking mire, egging each other on and getting out just in time, friends pulling hard on our arms as we struggled to free our legs from the grip of the sand.

Then there was the huge rusty sewer pipe which ran out into the waves. We'd leap from strut to strut without falling off into the putrid oily mud which lay on each side. At the end of the sewer pipe we would peer over into its dark cavernous mouth at the disgusting effluence disgorging into the sea. But when the tide was out we'd revisit the scene and bring back home bucketloads of baby crabs which we would race up and down our paths, until our mothers scolded us and made us take them back, or younger brothers stamped on the poor little creatures, their thin shells cracking, leaving squashed blobs of death on the crazy paving.

And it was worth the pain when our mothers vigorously scrubbed our oily legs clean with washing powder, the red weals apparent as we walked along the beach back to school in short white socks and highly-polished shoes.

Kevin Sampson   *Liverpool. Home*

Saturday, 15th September Five to ten in the morning. It's four days since the atrocities. Four days since the towers came down. Four extra days I've been stranded in New York City, penniless, just one of the stateless, homeless, nameless thousands, tramping Manhattan, using up time, waiting for better news.

Except I am not stateless. For years, many years, people have told me of the likeness between Liverpool, my city, and New York, theirs. I've been flattered by this – wanted to believe it. New York, the melting pot of the world, home to a thousand nations and a hundred different soundtracks, the twenty-five hour city that never sleeps. Liverpool, Manhattan in miniature, the seaboard city that throbs to its own beat. Everyone tells you they're sister states, linked by their maritime past.

But six thousand miles away, something is happening that only Liverpool knows. New York may have something else, something it holds similarly dear – but as the clock clunks close to ten, the last of the red and the blue clad hordes swarm anxiously to the Goodison turnstiles, ready for the latest episode in the greatest derby ever played; Liverpool against Everton.

Liverpool have just won five trophies in the space of a few

months, and they've started the season well. Everton are perennial under-performers. But supporters of either side would gladly settle out of court before proceedings begin, happy for a painless draw every time rather than the trauma of defeat at the hands of their bitter local rivals.

I trudge through Greenwich Village, looking for the bar I'm told might show the game. I was due to leave Manhattan on the afternoon of 9/11. I had taxi fare to get me to the airport, money for a coffee and a snack. How could I have any notion I'd still be here, days later? I had a ticket for this game – now I can't even afford a pint while I watch it on ESPN. That's if they're even showing it. I've been here in the great city of New York as one of the most horrific incidents in recent contemporary history unfolded and I'm aware that I'm nothing in the context of that tragedy... Yet my heart longs for home.

I want to be there, with the Redmen, cheering the lads on. I want the fear and the tension, the overpowering joy of the win, the supreme high of the walk out of the ground and across Stanley Park, a high that will last through a long night of drinking, and singing, deep into the week ahead. Everyone I know will be there – all my friends. To them – to myself, if I were there – it's a football match. One of the biggest, and one we're desperate to win – but it's The Match and it'll be over by five, and they'll all be looking forward to the next one.

Gillian Stone   *For love of property*

My friend has a house in Shanklin Road, a huge Georgian double fronted terrace house painted white. The chimney stacks are 30 feet high sailing into the sky. My dad told her to take them down. 'First big wind we have they'll blow right down'. 'Planning won't let us', she said. And that was the end of that.

There are a lot of beautiful houses in Wavertree, tucked away in tree-lined roads, hiding some of the newer developments. My dad likes Wavertree but much prefers Smithdown. He owns two houses in Bagot Street, bought over 20 years ago when he fell in love with them. Interest rates were 17% and we were penniless for years. He converted the double fronted Victorian terraces into luxury flats and drives past them lovingly on a daily basis. He'd love to live there but my dad plays the piano in the early hours of the morning. You can't do that when you live in a flat.

When they mended the roof he got up there himself. No mean feat for someone afraid of heights. I saw him when his shaky legs came down the ladder. He couldn't get over how high the houses were. Every so often he mutters 'Had to lower the ceilings though', before he explains the importance of fire regulations, sound proofing and the tenants being able to afford the gas bills. He thinks it is sacrilege to cover up the beauty of the plasterwork. My mum still has to comfort him. 'Don't worry, Joe,' she says comfortingly, 'they're still there under the false ceiling. Some day someone will strip off the ceiling and find cupids dancing on flowered coving and get the best surprise of their life.'

There are so many beautiful buildings in Liverpool, houses reminiscent of a grander age. I want to buy a house in Wavertree. I've seen one in Mill Lane. A late Georgian semi-detached with a side entrance and three long sandstone steps introducing you to an imposing front door. When I told my dad he had a glint in his eye 'There are some lovely old houses on Mill Lane, great big high ceilings with ribbons and swags, floating bunches of grapes, urns and ceiling roses.' He trailed off. 'One of those, I suppose?' And he looked at me and smiled.

Edward Mark Taylor   *First days*

I was five when we moved from Tuebrook to a large council house on the new Halewood estate. One of the picture windows in the large, and at that moment, bare, living room, looked out on a whole new world. It looked out on to a vast open field, swaying with high, pale-green grass, as far as my five year old eyes could see. To the left, this sea of grass was broken by a line of trees that swept upwards to a rounded green hill, where a lone tree stood. It was the country; it was the countryside, though I had no real idea what those words meant. I only knew it was a magical place, and I dreamt that night of foxes finding their way down the chimney and eating our food. It wasn't long before we were allowed out into this new world, for what parent in those days didn't let their children out to play? Our first tentative steps led us into this new and strange land. City children waist-high in green grass, on a great adventure.

The trees became known as the Woods. The hill unsurprisingly we called the Hill and its tree the Swing Tree. There was also the Monkey Tree, the Polio Pond and the Pyramids. The Pyramids were in fact tank traps, flat topped concrete blocks, left over from the war, scattered about a demolished railway bridge. From one pyramid you could swing out over the railway line that ran below. The look on passengers' faces as you flashed past was worth the terror of the leap. There were frogs, newts and small fish we called stickle-backs, to be taken home in jam jars. We fished, swam and climbed. We played hide-and-seek and fired imaginary guns at Nazzie (as we pronounced it) soldiers. It was the place of first girlfriends, first kisses and first cigarettes.

One morning, about ten years ago, I cycled along the tarmac path that had once been the train line and went in search of the Hill and the Swing Tree. The pitted walls of the demolished bridge were still there but the hill and tree were completely overgrown and not a pyramid was in sight. But the world that helped to form my childhood and populated my dreams remains with me to this day.

Kenneth Lockett   *Bohemian Liverpool*

Lark Lane is Bohemian Liverpool, and I want to live there. It's where writers and artists hang out. You see them sometimes drinking coffee in Keith's Wine Bar looking unconventional and arty like.

If you walk up the Lane from Aigburth Road, you don't see much at first, just cold tarmac where they set the stalls up for the Farmers' Market on the fourth Saturday of the month.

It's only when you reach Chilli Banana, the Thai Restaurant that's just opened (I can recommend the tapas) that you start to get a feel for the place. Next door is Elif, a Turkish BBQ Restaurant, by all accounts it's a cool place to eat as well.

Lark Lane's got everything, a one street village for dreamers with attitude. There's an upholstery and French polishing establishment, and a few doors away E Callister is a restorer of fine furniture. If Greek's your thing (it isn't mine at the moment because we've just lost 2-1 to AC Milan in Athens, but enough of that) then Romios' Taverna do it nicely. A little art gallery has opened, watch this space. There's a laundry and dry cleaning service, an old fashioned hardware shop, Paul cuts men's hair, women's too if you ask him. Home made cakes and pies (fantastic smells) are available, so is fresh fish and poultry next door, served by a Chinaman brimming with smiles and personality. For the gambling man a licensed betting office will relieve you of any spare cash; Retro, for the nostalgic; antiques and curios at Remains To Be Seen; fish and chips x two; Fallen Angle, a tattoo and body piercing emporium cuts it, metaphorically speaking.

WHITE STAR

Further on, towards Sefton Park, there's a retiring pizzeria with a sign in the window advertising 'Indian Take-Away opening soon', and across the road a hairdresser of exotic styles, a fireplace shop too. The old South Liverpool Police Headquarters is still there, the rozzers have moved on to more modern premises though; Baguette Bite, tables outside on the pavement; Vinyl, jazz club downstairs on Thursday's from nine o'clock; Pistachio, restaurant and bar; Que Pasa Cantina, another eatery. Right at the end of the Lane, where the garage used to be that serviced Rolls Royce and Bentleys, sixteen luxury apartments have sprouted (few remaining) the sign says.

Should my dream come true, and I live, then eventually pass away on Lark Lane, it just so happens that Charlett's Funeral Services are on hand to take care of the arrangements.

Brenda Muller   *Springtime Liverpool*

Longing for spring in Liverpool, full of nature's surprises. Hosts of golden daffodils in Sefton Park, planted in aid of Marie Curie Hospitals, are echoed by swathes of yellow on many roundabouts and roadside verges. Soon, there will be seas of bluebells in Childwall Woods and in the ancient woodlands of Otterspool. Stunning views of the River Mersey will be enjoyed by Sunday strollers on Otterspool promenade. On Princess Drive alternate trees of fresh green and bronze leaves are a tribute to whoever thought to plant them there. I love to see the many magnolias appearing in tiny front gardens providing beauty in unexpected places. Walks in the stunning parks of Liverpool are led almost daily by Park Rangers. Beware the Rangers! When they have seen you a few times on their walks, they will tease you if you don't remember the Latin names of all the plants and trees en route. All too soon, spring will turn to summer, and then autumn brings another longing to drive along Menlove Avenue and into Sefton Park for a feast of autumn tints.

Stephen Bayley *Liverpool 17 yr old*

I have lived in London three times as long as I lived on Merseyside, but still say I come from Liverpool. I rarely go back, but when I do, no map is required. Nearly 40 years after I left, it still provides the cityscape of my nightmares. No other city, not even New York or Venice, has such a powerful built environment. You cannot be reasonably alert and grow up here being complacent about architecture: there is so much of it. But it is a brooding presence: there is an epic melancholy about a city that has experienced such tumult. Liverpool has its comedians, but it is not always a happy place. For me, personally, it's full of ghosts. I blub when I hear *In My Life*.

In my Liverpool schooldays, the danger lurking on the streets was generally restricted to being nutted by a debilitated Guinness drinker. Now the demographic has changed. The big danger today is getting sideswiped by an espresso-demented loft dweller's Mercedes-Benz 320SLK. In my schooldays, the air was made of sulphur, shoeless waifs lined the streets, beggarwomen wailed outside Lime Street station. A bath was for storing coal. Baths are now full of seaweed and sage bodywash. They sell the Harvard Business Review at Smith's on Lime Street Station. But leaving Lime Street today you are still confronted by a contrasting spectacle that is utterly Liverpool in its incongruous mixture of swaggering magnificence and dismaying tat. Liverpool is beautiful and ugly, proud and wanton, impressive and dismaying, romantic and crass.

Twenty-six years after my wife's first visit we came back: a serious Londoner, she says she wants to come to live here. Liverpool is not a city you can feel neutral about.

Linda Kettle   *Day return*

It's hard to explain why I want to go to Liverpool. I mean, I never want to go anywhere in particular. I'm one of those home birds – you know the kind – who on going out for the day, can't wait to get back.

I've always shied of staying away overnight and cannot see the point of holidays... They're more a punishment than a treat.

So why the pull towards Liverpool?

I must confess that the appeal lies in a certain person who lives there and let's face it, there can only be one such character who is fairly famous and can boast that he himself (almost an octogenarian) actually still lives in the house where he was born.

You must have guessed... It's the Squire of Knotty Ash. What makes him tick? Is it true he has books in his place piled from floor to ceiling in four rooms? (I'd love to find out.)

It must be true that he prefers to sleep in his own bed. After performing on stage, he often comes home if he's within 100 miles of Liverpool rather than live it up in a hotel somewhere. After all, he could afford it.

There is no Spanish villa nor French apartment where he retreats, just a second much less-publicised home located vaguely in Cheshire. Neither is there a Bentley nor Aston Martin – merely a people carrier in which he travels with his driver and small entourage.

So who or what, fires the imagination of a man, who as one reporter puts it, has hardly ever left Merseyside except to star in his own shows?

Any interview he might give is conducted at a mutually agreed public venue, for no-one ever gets beyond the front door of his 1740's Georgian farmhouse.

But that's okay with me.

I'd simply like to go there, to Knotty Ash, to drink in the atmosphere (a dose of tickle tonic, maybe?) and know that I was standing on Professor Chucklebutty's famous giggling ground.

Anita Holmes   *Minding cars*

The loud pounding noise echoed through my chest. It came from the masses of men galloping down our street. They were like hordes of wildebeest on their way to a watering hole.

'Mind yer car mate'? 'Ok, Scouse'! Came the reply.

You had to be quick to let them know you were minding their car or they would disappear into the crowds and you wouldn't get paid.

Our street lead directly to Liverpool football ground and on match days at Anfield, most of the kids in our street would have a spec they called their own. Mine was outside my parents shop. My brothers had the olla. The olla was in the next street to ours. It was a large piece of waste ground that was once graced with houses but they were blown up during the Second World War.

There was something special about a match day in the 1970s. The street would be heaving with cars and people. Then all of a sudden it was like the *Marie Celeste*. But in the background you could clearly hear kick off time by the cheers and the singing.

One day when the match had started all the kids sat around. They were not really minding cars as they were supposed to be, but just passing time. Everyone was chatting and skitting each other and deciding what to spend their money on. All of a sudden one of the bigger lads, Eddie, jumped up like a bat out of hell, picked up Gary, one of the smaller lads, and dangled him by his feet. His screams were drowned by the laughter from the other boys and the thud of loose change hitting the ground. 'I knew he was sticking down on us, the little rat' shouted Eddie.

Gary spluttered and tried to explain but to no avail. Well that was it! That was the worst thing you could do. That was like stealing from your Nan's purse. What disgrace Gary had brought upon himself. When you are in a gang you must obey the gang's ethics or you're out and one of the rules was that all money earned from minding cars would be pooled so everybody got the same.

I will never forget that day and the fear that struck Gary's face. He never got to mind cars again.

That evening I treated myself to fish and chips and a can of coke for my tea.

Peter Goldsmith   *Somerset's case*

On the 24th January 1772 James Somerset was waiting to know his fate. He was a young African captured in his homeland and taken into slavery to the New World. There, in Virginia, he was sold to a merchant and slave trader, a Scot named Charles Steuart. James's condition was shared by countless other Africans. 'Torn from their natal shore, and doom'd to bear The yoke of servitude in western climes' as

Liverpool's William Roscoe, poet, banker, lawyer and politician, described the state of the slave trade at the time.

Brought to England, James escaped – but was recaptured. He was waiting on a ship in the Thames bound for Jamaica when a case was brought before the greatest judge in England, Lord Mansfield, to set James free.

This was a time of change. The clamour against the iniquity of the slave trade was growing; abolitionists such as Roscoe were writing, campaigning and, as in Somerset's case – as it came to be known – testing the limits of the law on slavery.

Liverpool had prospered from the slave trade. There are great houses and fine buildings which date back to those days. It is estimated that probably three-quarters of all European slaving ships in the late 18th century left from Liverpool. Overall, Liverpool ships transported half of the three million Africans carried across the Atlantic by British slavers.

Yet it is hard to think now of Liverpool of all places – tolerant, good humoured, hospitable Liverpool, proud and honourable Liverpool – as the place which made so much from such misery; whose prosperity owes so much to the longing of the slaves as they were transported in rough seas far from home to slavery with strangers. Let us remember them as Liverpool celebrates its 800th birthday in the same year as we commemorate the 200th anniversary of the legislation which finally outlawed the evil slave trade in 1807.

And what of the longing of James Somerset? Five months later on the 22nd June 1772 – 35 years before the 1807 abolition law – Lord Mansfield gave a short but momentous judgement: James Somerset was free.

Lorna Read   *Don't drive down Booker Avenue*

'Don't go there, it'll upset you.' That's what my friend Claire had said when she heard we were coming. It was 11th May 2007, fifteen years to the day since Dad died. My sister and I had travelled to Springwood Crematorium to pay our respects. We reminisced in the Hall of Remembrance, dabbed our eyes, popped over the road to de-moss the memorial stone, then sat on the bench behind it to eat our sandwiches.

'A picnic in the cemetery. That would have given Mum a giggle,' said my sister.

'Yes, I'm half expecting her spectral hand to pop up and snatch my sarnie,' I replied.

Our parents' was the only unadorned plot. With both of us living far away now, my sister in Cumbria and me in London, it seemed pointless to festoon it with flowers and cards like most people had done, as we weren't around to keep it tidy. Yet somehow, our stone had acquired a toy fairy.

Green, Mum's favourite colour.

'She probably thought, 'Huh! *They* couldn't be bothered to give me any ornaments so I'm having that,' and nicked it from someone else,' said my sister and we both burst out laughing.

Yet, at the back of my brain, my friend's warning was still ringing so, when Little Sis asked, 'What shall we do now?' I immediately said, 'Let's drive past 24 Booker.'

My parents had bought the house in 1949. We were brought up there and the house, pebble-dash and mock Tudor, had remained our family seat until 1997, when we sold it to a developer following Mum's death. We heard he'd sold it on to a family. We were happy about that. Mum would have liked children in the place.

Soon, we saw what Claire had meant. Sheets of metal were battened across the windows. The empty house looked like a corpse in a suit of armour. My heart lurched. 'Looks like it's been repossessed,' said my sister.

As we stared, scenes from my life ran backwards in my mind like a video on reverse: leaving for uni and my mum's sad face as she waved me off; my seventeenth birthday party where some divvy put olives in the tank and killed the goldfish; my first days at Booker Avenue Primary School, crying up the railway bridge then skipping down the other side as I spied all my little friends. How I longed for those days to return. I longed to have my parents, my childhood back again. I longed for the streets of Liverpool 18, the friendly faces, the shops where, even now, some people still remember us.

'I'm going to ring the estate agents and ask what's

happened,' I said.

My sister had been right. The house had been repossessed. We felt sad for the people. But it had been re-sold. Soon, I hope, the garden will ring with childish laughter again. And some of it will forever be ours.

David Rainbird · *Forty years on*

Can it really be nearly forty years since I first arrived in the city, naïve and idealistic, from Oxford University. I came to Lime Street Station on a steam train, which gives an idea as to how long ago it was.

My home town is actually Newcastle upon Tyne. Don't worry, people used to say: Liverpool is just like Newcastle. But it wasn't. It was (and remains in my view) completely different. One hundred and twenty ships, from Seaforth to the Dingle Buoys, and from Birkenhead to Bidston, served by 15,000 dockers. A buoyant, optimistic place; the Beatles, the football teams, full employment, with no hint of the disasters to come.

And I was in the middle of it all. I remember taking the old green municipal bus to my first flat in Princes Park, the street lights still slung on wires and cables over the road, and feeling a greater sense of freedom than at any time before or since. To the right were the old south docks, full of ships, shebeens and sailormen. The streets looked more dangerous than they were. A few weeks later, my girlfriend and I got lost around High Park Street. We were suddenly surrounded by a gang of towering black lads. Timorously we explained our predicament. They insisted on taking us to the bus stop, and telling us clearly how to get home. I developed a great affection for Liverpool 8 (or Toxteth, as it is now wrongly called), which remains with me today.

Only slightly further away was Chinatown, the first I had ever seen. Just next to it again was the still incomplete Anglican Cathedral, from whose steps, on my first Friday night, I watched as the last great transatlantic liner, the *Empress of Canada*, sailed for Montreal.

Things change. Longing for the past is pointless, and in any case living through something, and looking back on it, is entirely different. Even so, it's hard not to regret the passing of the ships, the seafarers, and the dockers. If Liverpool is not a great port, what is it?

Dave Calder   *Unravelling*

How long is longing?

Its geometry is not so much a fixed length, as in: how long is it on foot between the Everyman and Somali by way of O'Connors, Pilgrim, Cracke and Peter Kavanaghs: it is not only distance but time, is more a loop, a circular walk around the blocks, a pattern mapped and woven into the mind: from Brownlow Hill by way of Crown and Granby to Princes Park, through to Ullet back by Devonshire and Princes Avenue, round the Anglican to Rodney and Mount Pleasant. And how long is that then? About twenty five years. Caught in the net of remembered streets we dream of what was, perhaps, and prolong desire.

Draw in the noose: up Canning Street to Falkner Square, down Husky, back along Catherine, Percy or Gambier depending on which memory is being visited. This is both punishment and luxury. To long is to belong to the past, for if the houses appear much the same, the rooms will be different; friends and lovers no longer inhabit these spaces except in your mind. The knot tightens on the heart.

On the long journey, with good fortune, we will conquer fear and anger. Perhaps also we may learn to live without longing.

Gillian Reynolds   *Dream river*

It is the Mersey I think of, long for. It isn't even a conscious longing. I'll be thinking about something else and suddenly

smell salt, see the river. Sometimes it's sparkling, under a blue sky and a little breeze, seen from the top deck of the ferry. Sometimes it's mud brown, churning under a gale, heaving, hitting the walls of the landing stage in great fat slaps, sending big drops all over you as you look down at it. I remember it in winter, crossing over to the old Woodside Station in Birkenhead to catch the day's one through train to Oxford, the 9.20 am (If you went from Lime Street there was always a change at Bletchley and maybe one before, at Crewe, as well). I see a frosty, misty morning, very still. The boat comes in, looming out of the mist to turn sideways and tie up. The river is quiet, grey. It makes smaller sounds than usual under the ferry, like small suckings of a straw reaching the bottom of a bottle, as we cross the veiled river in once-only wonder.

Chris High   *No escape*

The hottest day of the year and the crowds weren't helping. What a *stupid* time – what a stupid *day* – to arrange a meeting but that's what you get for trying to predict the unpredictable.

I checked my watch. One-thirty. The portfolio presentation at John Moores University was at two so, hopefully, I prayed, it wouldn't take long and I'd miss the main event.

Shuffling down the steps of Lime Street Station, a recent operation on my back making swift progress impossible, I decided on grabbing a cab to my destination.

I was in luck. Outside the 'Under Refurbishment' banners of St George's Hall, taxis stood like shining troop carriers, their paintwork gleaming. I clambered, muttering, into the nearest.

'The Anglican?' the driver asked. 'Now, that's the one up by the –'

'Listen,' I said. 'I'm not a bloody tourist, okay?'

The glass the partition slid closed.

Outside, the crowds were growing.

I checked my watch.

Bloody hell.

Eleven minutes and twelve quid later, I headed into the building. After two hours, fifty minutes, I hobbled into the sunshine again, its glare illuminating the cathedral as though it were a star on stage.

Red bricks. Typical.

Hobbling along Rodney Street then turning left, past St Luke's bombed out church and on to Bold Street, I moved through crowds that were now treacle thick.

Bloody Gerry Marsden, I thought. *Bloody Carousel.*

At last, I turned off Bold Street into Central Station.

Oh no, the posters *had* to be wrong. God didn't hate me *that* much, surely?

He did. All trains and buses, 'cancelled' the posters said.

Out of the station, desperate, the roads heaving with people waving flags and scarves, singing that God-awful song over and over again. I needed sanctuary; a quiet pub... one into which I could escape.

No chance. Bloody hell, there were idiots standing on the arched roof of Lime Street Station, so there was no chance of getting to stand at a bar.

Lime Street proper heaved like an out of breath dragon and pushing through onto London Road proved impossible. Somebody had tied a scarf – red and white – around Wellington's granite waist and I felt as trapped as the stone lions in their cages, opposite.

Four hours and countless renditions of that *bloody* song later, the open-topped bus finally crawled into view, with more people on board than a Calcutta tram.

The noise from the masses as deafening as a Motorhead gig only less tuneful, my misery became complete, with Steven Gerrard delivering the coup de grâce.

Standing on the top deck, the trophy glinting in his hands, the skipper raised it high, pointed into the crowd – pointed at *me,* I'm convinced – and winked.

Even amongst the dancing thousands, it seemed there was

no place for a Manchester United fan to hide that night and, as Liverpool brought home their fifth European Cup, I longed to be anywhere else than here.

Brean Hammond   *Pointed stick*

1989. A man is walking down Rose Lane carrying a piece of two by two, about six feet long, and sharpened at one end. He's just bought the wood from the DIY shop at the railway bridge – an Aladdin's cave whose female custodian knows far more about DIY than most men ever will. Feeling faintly emasculated, he goes into the butcher's to buy some mince. 'You come into a butcher's, and you bring your own steak', quips the butcher. Back on the street, 'Jeez, the vampires round your place must be huge, la.' 'You'll get done for carrying an offensive weapon', says a third passer-by. No-one can resist the spectacle of a man walking down the street with a pointed stake. The man smiles wanly. He's melancholy because he is leaving Liverpool. He is constructing a bird-table, as a memorial for his recently deceased wife. And he now knows what he will miss when he is elsewhere.

Mary Braithwaite   *Wales is the horizon*

Escaping from the surging crowds of Liverpool, I press towards the ferry point. Beyond is the coast of West Kirby or the beach of New Brighton to paint with my water colours.

By the river, gulls are gliding and diving, screeching like new-born babies. At last, on the Mersey ferry. I take a deck seat and the salt breeze blows away the stress.

The water is dappled in grey and silver and slate and also channels and sprays from the helm. Soon I will be on the bus to West Kirby where the horizon is the mountains of Wales.

Yoko Ono Lennon   *Liddypool John*

One day, in the autumn of 1967, I went to Liverpool for the first time, invited by Liverpool Art School. I had a great time, went back to London, and reported to John immediately. 'Oh, so you went. How did you like it?' He sounded mighty proud of the city. Though I met him in London, I never forgot that my husband was a Liverpudlian. That side of him was so wonderful – such great fun. Even in the darkest moment in our lives, he would say something funny, and make me crack up. Quite something, that was.

Those days are over. And I miss it. Now, whenever I think of Liverpool, I can't help thinking of John's modest child-hood bedroom in Mendips. That was where it all started. It still chokes me up every time I visit that room.

So I'd like to share a very special lullaby with you. I'm sure John would have wanted me to do that. It's a lovely and sweet lullaby not commonly known outside of Liverpool. But it is the one my husband loved. Yes. He was a Liverpool boy all the way, even after we moved to NY. Even in the very last year of his life, he sang this song to his son, Sean, every night after tucking him in bed. You know what John was thinking about in those moments? It was LIVERPOOL, I'm sure.

Oh Liverpool Lou, lovely Liverpool Lou
Why don't you behave just like other girls do
Why must my poor heart keep following you
Stay home and love me, my Liverpool Lou

When I go a-walking I hear people talking
Schoolchildren playing, I know what they're saying
They're saying you'll grieve me, that you will deceive me
Some morning you'll leave me, all packed up and gone

The sounds from the river keep telling me ever
That I should forget you like I'd never met you
Tell me this song, love, was never more wrong, love
Say I belong, love, to my Liverpool Lou.

BIOGRAPHIES

Nicholas ALLT is a writer from Kirkby who has published books about the misadventures of Liverpool FC fans; he also writes for newspapers and magazines.

Will ALSOP is a renowned architect whose winning 'Fourth Grace' design for the Liverpool waterfront, *The Cloud,* was controversially dropped in 2004.

Tayo ALUKO is an architect and property developer who was born in Nigeria and came to Liverpool in 1989; he is also a versatile singer, performer and playwright.

William BACKSHALL was born in Litherland and had a varied career at sea and on the docks and was self-employed until his retirement; he now lives in Lydiate.

Angela BARLOW was born in Bolton and first visited Liverpool as a seven year-old; she moved here in 2004 and is now a learning assistant at National Museums Liverpool.

David BATEMAN was born in Kent, came to Liverpool in 1980 and is a poet (2007 Liverpool Poetry Slam Champion), performer and creative writing tutor.

Stephen BAYLEY moved to Liverpool as a toddler, and later studied architecture here; a well-known cultural observer, he set up London's Design Museum in 1989.

Jane BELLIS was born in Wrexham, came to Liverpool to study and then left but has recently returned to work as a youth engagement officer at Greenbank College.

Joanne BENFORD is a creative writing tutor, novelist, poet, artist and musician in Hartlepool; she has a keen interest in Liverpool's architecture and shipping heritage.

Lewis BIGGS came to Liverpool in 1987 as curator at the Tate Gallery and is now director of the Liverpool Biennial, Britain's largest contemporary arts festival.

Jane BRADLEY is a freelance journalist and fiction writer now living in London; she was born in Liverpool, moved to Manchester at the age of six, but returns often.

Mary BRAITHWAITE moved to Merseyside 30 years ago from Surrey, raised her family and launched a painting and writing career late in life; she lives in Southport.

Shirley BUCKLEY is from Kirkby where her family still lives; she left to go to Sheffield University and has been a modern languages teacher in London for twenty years.

Clare BUNTING was born in Leamington Spa, and returned there to work in publishing after studying imaginative writing at Liverpool John Moores University.

Dave CALDER came to Liverpool in 1964 to read law but became involved in community arts – from 1976 with the Windows Project; he is now a poet in Scotland.

Ramsey CAMPBELL was born in Liverpool, sold his first story while still at school and is now one of world's most celebrated horror writers; he is also a film critic.

Mathew CAPPER was born on the Wirral and has lived in Liverpool for 12 years; he is a drugs worker, and also an actor who has written and directed short films here.

Liam Patrick COÀN was born in Liverpool, studied history at Liverpool John Moores University and joined Merseyside Police as a community support officer.

Gladys Mary COLES is a respected Liverpool Welsh poet who has published over ten collections of poetry and an anthology of local poetry, prose and drama, *Both Sides of the River*.

Frank COTTRELL-BOYCE is a screenwriter and novelist from Liverpool with many film credits; he started his writing career on the TV soap Brookside in the 1980s.

Terence DAVIES is a film director who explores his 1940s and 50s working-class Liverpool background in several of his films, most notably *Distant Voices Still Lives*.

Wendy DAVIES is an administration assistant who lives in Montgomery, Powys, but who spent her first seventeen years in Liverpool and still visits regularly.

Bronwyn DAVIS is from Adelaide, Australia and has also lived in Canberra; she came to Liverpool in August 2006 and works as an advisor for the Citizens' Advice Bureau.

David DOWLING is a youth worker who was born and lives in Liverpool; in 2005-6 he took part in the Round the World Yacht Race, crewing on the *Liverpool 08* yacht.

Francis DUFFY is a history teacher born and raised in the Dingle area of Liverpool; he has also written plays which have been performed locally and filmed for TV.

Philip FERGUSON is currently in HMP Liverpool; he responded to an item in *Inside Time* about the Mersey Minis writing competition.

Ranulph FIENNES is a mountaineer and explorer who has led expeditions to both poles, climbed the Eiger and raised millions for charities; he lives in Cheshire and has family in Liverpool.

Karoline FRITZSCH is a translation student from Halle, near Leipzig in eastern Germany, who came to Liverpool on a sabbatical in 2005 and has settled in the city.

Christopher GEORGE was born in Liverpool and emigrated to the United States as a child; he is a poet, editor and contributor to online and print magazines.

Helen GLASSPOOLE was born in Hereford, came to university in Liverpool and is now a lecturer of education with many text books and teaching resources to her credit.

Peter GOLDSMITH is a former Quarry Bank, Liverpool, pupil who was Attorney General, the government's most senior lawyer, from 2001 to June 2007.

Niall GRIFFITHS is a novelist who was born in Liverpool into a Welsh family, now lives in Wales and uses both places as settings in his visceral novels.

Loyd GROSSMAN was born in Boston, USA but has worked mainly in UK media and cultural industries; he is also chair of National Museums Liverpool and a keen advocate for the city.

Sue HAASLER was born in County Durham, but a passion for Liverpool FC often brings her to the city; she lives in Hertfordshire and has published three novels.

Brean HAMMOND is professor of Modern English Literature at the University of Nottingham; he was born in Edinburgh but lived in Liverpool from 1976 to 1990.

Chris HIGH is a freelance journalist, reviewer and sessional lecturer at Liverpool John Moores University; he was born in Liverpool and now lives on the Wirral.

Anita HOLMES is Liverpool born and bred, left school early but returned as a mature student to Liverpool Community College where she is now a support officer.

Mike HYDE is a retired civil engineer, born in Keighley, Yorkshire, now living in Kendal but lived in Liverpool as a child and worked in the city between 1957 and 1965.

Ted JONES is an Everton fan who lives in Windsor but was born and raised in Walton; a retired accountant, he has written a literary guide to the French Riviera.

Linda KETTLE is a piano teacher in Portsmouth, who has no connection to Liverpool other than an interest in the Liverpool Poets and as a fan of Ken Dodd.

Karen LAMB is an illustrator, scriptwriter and animator who has worked extensively in Sweden but now lives in Blackpool and visits her partner in Liverpool regularly.

Tony LANE was a merchant seamen who first came to Liverpool in 1956, later 'swallowing the anchor' to become a sociology lecturer at the University of Liverpool.

Kenneth LOCKETT is an engineer from Doncaster who moved to Liverpool in 2006; previously he lived in North Wales but had been visiting the city since 1998.

Nigel MALPASS is a marine consultant from Manchester, now living in the Isle of Man; he was a ship's captain with the Liverpool-based Bibby Line for many years.

Leto MARTINOU KYRITSI is a biologist who was born and lives in Athens; she lived in Liverpool between 1996 and 2004 while studying and working at the University.

Margo McDONOUGH is a retired tutor from Huyton who

has always lived in Liverpool; after working in a bookshop for twenty years she took a literature degree.

Gill McEVOY is a writer born in London, now living in Chester, who has worked in Liverpool; she is a published poet and regular visitor to the Dead Good Poet's Society.

Roger McGOUGH is a radio presenter and well-loved performance poet who came to prominence in 1967 with the Liverpool poetry collection *The Mersey Sound.*

Michèle McGRATH is a retired careers service manager from the Isle of Man; she lived in Liverpool for eight years and regularly visited her mother's family here.

Stephen McKAY is a Sheffield-born chemist, currently in Hull but planning to return to Liverpool, where he has been involved in local arts and heritage for twenty years.

Walter MENZIES was born in Edinburgh but worked on Merseyside in sustainability and urban regeneration and is now chief executive of the Mersey Basin Campaign.

Jan MINTING was born in Anfield, the daughter of magician Roy Minting, grew up in Huyton; she now runs a fancy dress shop in Oldham and sings with her sisters.

Jennifer MOORE was born in Bournemouth and lives near Plymouth; she visited Liverpool with her family 15 years ago and would like to return one day.

Phil MORRIS was born and grew up on Merseyside, left for a while but returned seven years ago to Liverpool where he now lives and works as a marketing manager for the NHS.

David MORRISSEY is a Liverpool-born film and TV actor who began at the Everyman Youth Theatre, making his television debut in Willy Russell's *One Summer* in 1983.

Brenda MULLER has always lived in Liverpool; she worked at Rushworth's Music House for twenty years and is now a librarian at Central Library Record Office.

Margaret MURPHY is a crime writer who uses her native Liverpool as a setting in some of her novels; she turned to full time writing after a career as a science teacher.

Betty NORTON was born in Liverpool, left at 16 to train as a cadet nurse at Clatterbridge Hospital on the Wirral, and is now retired and living in Preston.

Gill NORTON is a retired biology teacher who was born in Hoylake and grew up in New Brighton looking across the River Mersey to Liverpool every day.

Thomas NORTON was born in Birkenhead, studied sociology at the University of Liverpool, was in business, travelled the world and has now retired to Hoylake.

Yoko ONO LENNON is an artist and musician who was born in Japan and lives in New York but her connection with Liverpool goes back to the 1960s when she met and married Beatle John Lennon.

Szilvia OPAVSZKI lives in Hungary where she teaches English as a Foreign Language, but she has family and friends in Liverpool and has visited many times.

Dea PARKIN is a copywriter and marketing consultant in Chorley; she has clients in Liverpool and visits for both business and pleasure and is also writing a novel.

David PEARCE was born in Cardiff but grew up in Accrington; he moved to Merseyside in 1973 for a teaching post but took early retirement on health grounds in 1988.

Catherine PETERS is a documentary filmmaker in London who was born and bred in Liverpool; she left at 18 to go to university, but returns frequently to visit her family.

Roger PHILLIPS grew up in Manchester and is a well-known voice on BBC Radio Merseyside, where he has worked since the 1970s after a spell as an actor at the Everyman Theatre.

David RAINBIRD was born in Gateshead, Tyne & Wear but has lived on Merseyside for 39 years where he was a history and politics teacher, and is now semi-retired.

Lorna READ is a book editor and author from Middlesex; she lived in Liverpool until she was 22, and has published a number of children's books, fiction and short stories.

Gillian REYNOLDS is a Liverpool-born journalist, radio critic and broadcaster who was the first woman programme controller for a commercial radio station, Radio City.

Thomas RILEY was born in Liverpool and brought up in orphanages before leaving to work in the electronics and radar industries; he is now retired and living in Sussex.

Kevin SAMPSON is a Liverpool writer who started writing for music and youth magazines in the 1980s; he has now published several novels about football and urban culture.

Diane SAMUELS was born in Liverpool and is a playwright and author whose work includes *Kindertransport*, a play about the rescue of Jewish children from Nazi Germany.

Matt SIMPSON was born in Bootle and lectured in English at what is now Liverpool Hope University; he has published seven poetry collections and much literary criticism.

Deborah SINGMASTER is a Dublin-born architectural journalist who lives in London but who visited Liverpool many times on assignment; she now produces audio walks.

Jeanette SMITH was born in Carlisle but has lived on Merseyside since she was a baby; she has been a local journalist since 1966 and is now a lecturer in journalism.

Catherine SPARKS runs an on-line used books business and has just moved back to Liverpool from Birkenhead; she has also been a teacher and market stall holder.

Gillian STONE is a mother of two and solicitor who, apart from a spell in Manchester, has always lived and worked in Liverpool; she has now set up her own commercial practice.

David SWIFT is a Liverpool-born actor best known for his role in the comedy series *Drop the Dead Donkey*; he lives in London but with his wife Paula remains a major supporter of the arts in Liverpool.

Edward Mark TAYLOR is a Royal Mail manager from Liverpool who has also published a children's story *The Long Journey Home,* a Christmas story for the whole family.

John THACKRAY was born in Liverpool and now lives in Birkenhead, having moved there after he was married in 1972; he is a data telecoms engineer for telent in Chorley.

Gill TORRES was born and brought up on Merseyside but now lives in Liverpool; she is as a marketing executive with an MA in Screenwriting and has short films in production.

Mhairi TYNAN was born in Blackpool and grew up in Kent where she still lives; she visited her father's Liverpool family regularly, the last time was for her Granny's funeral.

Dave WARD was born in Northampton and has lived in Liverpool since 1971; he is a poet who co-founded the Windows Project, running writing workshops since 1976.

Christine WEBB was born in London, lives in Kent and has no link with Liverpool other than a desire to indulge her passion for bell ringing in the Anglican Cathedral.

David Alan WILLIAMS is a retired marine insurance underwriter who was born and educated in Liverpool, left to see the world in 1966 and now lives in Leicestershire.

Matthew WILLIAMS was born and brought up on Merseyside; he is currently at HMP Dovegate, Staffordshire.

Jeff YOUNG is a writer who was born in Liverpool and began writing for theatre and radio in 1986; he is currently writing for various BBC TV dramas including *Eastenders*.

JUDGES' COMMENTS

THERE ARE THINGS you forget about Liverpool. That steep dark descent as your train comes into Lime Street, for example, through what Fritz Spiegl called the caverns. An entrance that demands big opening lines; and there they are, in the grandstanding grandeur of St George's Hall, asking in the Scouse way – friendly, but a bit challenging, too – 'All right, pal?' Somehow, it surprises you every time.

Other surprises for a born-but-long-left, semi-detached Scouser: how good some of the entries were, and how bold and confident even the bad ones were. But that's the Scouse way, too, isn't it? Nothing by halves.

This is me from elsewhere: 'I've always liked Scousers, with the admiration of the timid for the daring, of the man below for the high-wire artist; in this case, high-wire artists of the over-dramatic, the anarchic and the riskily sentimental.' The competition entries were like that, even from the non-Scousers: some pulled it off, as you can see; others didn't.

But they had a go. It's the effect of this place. The energy and anarchy that comes from being a port, the air alive now with the sound of drills and gulls, the call of the new meeting the call of the old. The wit and the wackiness, too, came through in the writing, often with the sardonic touch that's part of here as much as the sentiment, the Lennon to the McCartney.

The biggest surprise of all, though, would be the the world beyond the caverns overcoming its nervous suspicions of all this and taking the plunge into the Liverpool we know it would love. All right, pal?

CHARLES NEVIN

SO THERE WE WERE, three strangers, sitting around a table in Liverpool's Athenaeum, sandwiches to the left, coffee to the right, and a pile of manuscripts between us. After ten years of editing *The Reader* magazine and two previous stints as a literary competition judge, when I was asked this time I was swayed towards 'Yes' by the hope there might be a great Mersey voice out there. If there was, I was longing to hear it.

As in any open competition 'not good enough' was the biggest pile. Some hit the 'no' pile because we had limited space and someone else had written a similar piece in a slightly better way. Advice: be original or work harder. Those writers who only hear or reproduce their own voices (and only want to read their own work) often write with a tin ear and aren't interesting enough for others to read. Advice: read widely and keep reading.

'Good enough' was more varied. Some pieces stood out because they were both well done and had something to say. Others were included because – after all this was Liverpool – they just had great stories. Still others were irresistible because they recorded lost Liverpool, or shared memories.

As the afternoon wore on and we worked our way through our sandwiches, coffee, preferences and disagreements I realised that it was not about finding one superb voice, but more like auditioning people for a place in a choir. Heard all together, the voices we selected are the massed choir of the Liverpool experience. It's a moving and terrific sound, and one I hadn't realised I was waiting to hear.

JANE DAVIS

PUBLISHERS' NOTES

The new writing competition has been a delight: we have been overwhelmed by the entries' charm, honesty and feeling. We've also had tremendous support; particularly from Kate Gorst of Altru Drama who ran the writing workshops with her characteristic energy and passion; and from BBC Radio Merseyside.

Each piece has been freshly written for LONGING in 2007, completing eight centuries of writing about this city.

I'M NOT FROM ROUND HERE, you see, so I watch the influx, exodus.

The city chiding, challenging. Looking inwards at family and friends, community. Accents, expression. Looking out; at one with the world again.

Contrary; teasing and testing. At once angry and smiling; aggressive and sentimental. Cool as a cucumber, passionate. Partisan. Hot as hell. I shop in my pyjamas but I work it like a WAG when I touch town.

Hard, soft. The good, the bad, the ugly. Hopes and ambition bring us building sites and the Big Dig. But are we beaten now, or better? Boring? Never. Magnificent Liverpool, Liverpool munificent...

It's only when you go that you know. And then at Lime Street I am home; inside the influx.

Liverpool is the grit under my skin. Niggling. Testing. Raw. Pure. Satisfying. I know I'm alive here.

FIONA SHAW

'MAY YOU LIVE in interesting times.' This wry wish is said to be a curse in China, but for Liverpool, from me, it is a heartfelt prayer.

People yearn for peace and contentment; we want to be happy, we want to have made it. But the more damning Chinese curse is 'May you find what you're looking for.' Once you've made it, what more is there to do apart from fighting to keep it? – or, of course, to lose it.

Liverpool was, for several lifetimes, one of the world's greatest trading cities, wielding power way beyond the imagination of King John's merchants. But it didn't last. The loss of influence and wealth have, in living memories, spawned despair, rage, apathy, bitterness. But one thing I've learned from producing books about this city is that Liverpool is on a long adventure. The path twists, sometimes heading several ways at once, so that people and events drift apart, and collide with stunning force.

Those collisions make sparks. The sparks can become rockets, or flares, or fires. They can create or destroy, a gentle warmth, or bright enough to light up the world – but this is urban life at its most exciting.

This city is a place like few others: never, ever bland. Frustrating, and bewildering, and the cause of grey hair and ulcers if you take too much notice of the daily news. But rich in ways most people wouldn't understand. Peaceful? god, no. Some say it's one long car crash.

But the city is racing again. Relish the ride. Liverpool is the dodgems, not a motorway; but despite the bruises, the buzz is addictive.

ARABELLA MCINTYRE-BROWN

ILLUSTRATIONS

These striking illustrations were commissioned for Mersey Minis from artist Clare Curtis, and present her unique visual response to Liverpool. Clare follows a long tradition of British printmakers with her distinctive linocuts, which are imbued with a bold, contemporary feel. Felixstowe-based Clare demonstrates her empathy with the sea with maritime patterns and motifs appearing throughout her work.

These specially commissioned icons have been chosen for their multi-layered local references.

Liver Bird: Originally the Eagle of St John the Divine, the bird evolved after the Civil War into Liverpool's mythical guardian, carrying a bit of seaweed rather than Plantagenet King John's symbol of *planta genista*, or broom.

Pub sign: Representing a favoured social pastime of locals and visitors alike, we have chosen not only a famous city centre pub, but a historic Liverpool shipping name with strongly emotional associations as the owner of *Titanic*.

Steam train: Stephenson won the Rainhill Trials with *Rocket* in 1829, for the world's first passenger railway line (Liverpool to Manchester); classic toys Hornby Trains and Meccano were invented in Liverpool.

Cotton: Bound up with the city's fortunes – cotton picked by slaves transported by Liverpool ships, trade links with India and Egypt; even today 70% of world cotton for export is sold under Liverpool arbitration.

Music: Liverpool boasts world-class music from sea shanties to the Royal Liverpool Philharmonic; Merseybeat hit international consciousness in the 1960s, but owes its heritage to cultures from around the world

Neptune: Roman God of the Sea, mythical feature on the city coat of arms; the planet Neptune was the final home of the highly evolved human race in local writer Olaf Stapledon's *Last and First Men*.

Oak leaves: Quintessentially English; the Allerton Oak (over 1,000 years old); timber exports from Liverpool; the district of Aigburth means 'grove of oaks'; oak timbers were used to build ships on the Mersey.

INDEX OF AUTHORS

THE MERSEY MINIS COLLECTION

LONGING is the third of five volumes in the Mersey Minis series, published during 2007, Liverpool's 800th anniversary year. The other four volumes – LANDING, LIVING, LOVING, LEAVING – are anthologies of writing from the past eight centuries of the city's recorded history.

To find out more about the Mersey Minis series, log on to www.merseyminis.com or email merseyminis@capsica.net

THE EDITOR

Though a land-lubber herself, Deborah Mulhearn was born in Liverpool into a family with a typically seafaring tradition.

She left school at 16 and worked in the wardrobe department of the Liverpool Playhouse. She then went back to formal education, studying English Literature at the University of Liverpool.

After the requisite stint in London, where she worked for five years in publishing and as a journalist on the Architects' Journal, she returned to Liverpool in 1991 to pursue a freelance career in journalism. She writes for a wide variety of newspapers and magazines and has contributed to several books on architecture, history and environment.

THE JUDGES

Jane DAVIS is the Director of The Reader, an outreach unit at the University of Liverpool; she grew up in Liverpool, went to school very unsuccessfully at Blackburn House and Quarry Bank and read English at the University of Liverpool in her twenties.
www.thereader.co.uk and www.getintoreading.org

Charles NEVIN is a Fleet Street journalist, humorist, columnist, travel writer and author of *Lancashire, Where Women Die of Love*, who was born in Liverpool to a Lancashire father and London mother, though he grew up in St Helens.